Some Inherited Disorders
of Brain and Muscle

Some Inherited Disorders of Brain and Muscle

*Proceedings of The Fifth Symposium of
The Society for the Study of Inborn
Errors of Metabolism*

Edited by
J. D. ALLAN & D. N. RAINE

E. & S. LIVINGSTONE LTD

EDINBURGH AND LONDON

1969

The editors wish to express the gratitude of all the members of the Society for the generous grants which have been received in support of this symposium from Mr. J. Milner and Scientific Hospital Supplies Limited, Liverpool.

SBN 443 00625 3

Printed in Great Britain

PREFACE

1967 marked the quinquennium of the Society and this year we ventured north to Newcastle for our Annual Symposium.

The meeting was well attended and the proceedings, following the precedent of the Dublin meeting in 1966, covered two days.

One was aware of the driving freshness of this northern university and city, and this spirit and freshness permeated the meeting.

The scientific papers were of high standard and led to discussion, which was provocative, informative and stimulating.

At our annual dinner and throughout the meeting we enjoyed the wonderful hospitality, traditional to the "Geordie".

We now are privileged to present the proceedings, and we hope that in fulfilling our task as Editors we have maintained the standard set by the speakers. To them and to all who took part in the discussion, we are deeply indebted. It is a basic trust of the Society to attempt to spread knowledge through the various disciplines concerned with the field of Inborn Errors and we hope that in this presentation we have succeeded in this aspect.

We wish to take this opportunity to express the gratitude of all members of the Society for generous grants on which this work is much dependant, donated by Scientific Hospital Supplies Ltd., of Liverpool, and in particular to thank Mr. J. Milner of this firm whose vision, drive and enthusiasm have been a constant encouragement.

Macclesfield   J.D.A.
　　1968   N.R.

PARTICIPANTS IN SYMPOSIUM

DR. J. D. ALLAN
West Park Hospital, Macclesfield.

DR. E. M. BRETT
Hospital for Sick Children, Great Ormond Street, London.

DR. V. DUBOWITZ
Department of Child Health, University of Sheffield.

DR. P. HUDGSON
Muscular Dystrophy Group Laboratories, Newcastle upon Tyne.

PROFESSOR J. H. HUTCHISON
Department of Child Health, University of Glasgow.

DR. H. JATZKEWITZ
Max-Planck Institute, Munich

DR. F. A. JENNER
Department of Biochemistry, Birmingham Children's Hospital.

DR. B. MCARDLE
Department of Chemical Pathology, Guy's Hospital, London.

DR. R. M. NORMAN
The Burden Neuropathological Laboratory, Frenchay Hospital, Bristol.

DR. R. J. PENNINGTON
Department of Clinical Biochemistry, University of Newcastle upon Tyne.

DR. R. J. POLLIT
Department of Biochemistry, Birmingham Children's Hospital.

DR. D. N. RAINE
Department of Biochemistry, Birmingham Children's Hospital.

PROFESSOR M. ROTH
Department of Psychological Medicine, University of Newcastle upon Tyne.

DR. J. M. WALSHE
Department of Investigative Medicine, Cambridge University.

DR. J. N. WALTON
Regional Neurological Centre, General Hospital, Newcastle upon Tyne.

DR. J. WILSON
Hospital for Sick Children, Great Ormond Street, London.

CONTENTS

Opening Remarks, President of the Society   *J. D. Allan*   ..   viii

Clinical Considerations in the Classification and Differential Diagnosis of Muscular Dystrophy   *J. N. Walton*   ..   1

Biochemical Abnormalities in Muscular Dystrophy
R. J. Pennington   23

Chemical and Structural Changes in Muscle: the Importance of the Nervous System   *V. Dubowitz*   32

Skeletal Muscle Glycogenoses other than Type II   *B. McArdle*   46

Type II (Pompe's) Skeletal Muscle Glycogenosis   *P. Hudgson*   60

Two New Inborn Errors of Metabolism?   *R. J. Pollit and F. A. Jenner*   78

The Nomenclature and Function of Lipid Molecules
D. N. Raine   82

Biochemical Classification of the Sphingolipidoses
D. N. Raine   89

Neuropathological Aspects of Some Cerebral Lipidoses
R. M. Norman   102

Cerebral Sphingolipidoses as Inborn Errors of Metabolism
H. Jatzkewitz   114

Some Observations on the Natural History of Wilson's Disease
J. M. Walshe   ..   ·   130

Clinical Aspects of Inherited Brain Disorders   *E. M. Brett* ..   141

The Genetics of Neuromuscular Disorders   *J. Wilson*   ..   151

OPENING REMARKS

MAY I first welcome everyone, especially our guests, Chairmen, and Speakers to this Symposium, and may I also say how pleased we all are and how honoured we feel to be holding our Meeting in this Northern University, which recently in more ways than one, has been establishing something of a reputation. In that this is our fifth Symposium, we are beginning to feel, though still with considerable reservation, that perhaps we are emerging from the chrysalis stage to one of independent existence.

These reservations, however, are very real and related to, in my mind at least, great humility. A humility which derives from the realisation of the limited individual intellectual conceptualisation in the light of the immensity of knowledge now accruing and always accelerating in so many fields to-day. When Garrod first established the new entity of Inborn Errors, though it was an immensely important break-through, the field remained essentially small and to most physicians, essentially obscure.

Even 10 years ago this was still so.

But synchronous with the break-through in chromosomes and heralded in by the new concept of phenylketonuria, has come a veritable flood of new ideas and new knowledge —the concept of medicine has completely altered. It is not any longer a question of calibrating disease of any type by the phenotype—we are profoundly affected in our approach by the genotype and the study of inborn errors is not any longer in any sense a somewhat restricted concept, but in its essence, a study, related as it is to molecular biology, of every system of the body. So humility we must I think feel inevitably but we must also feel anxiety—can Societies such as ours continue to exist in this era of outmoded bureaucracy—will the public sponsor the centres and nurture the brains to work on and reap the harvest. To carry this torch we need all the Henry Miller's and as many like him as we can muster. The image of the N.H.S. is not improving but times have been worse and truth has triumphed.

Mendel caught up in the financial intricacies of bureaucratic confusion, might have achieved much more but his efforts were not lost.

Lavoisier lived at a time when all the world as he knew it was breaking up and indeed he himself perished on the Guillotine. Yet he then had the courage to write as follows: "one can deserve well of one's fellow men without being a brilliant public figure. A doctor can serve his country by working quietly in his Laboratory or study and he can even hope by doing so to reduce to some extent the mass of human misery and to increase the joy and happiness of mankind. He may indeed discover something—who knows— which will add a few days or better still, a few years, to man's expectation of life".

Thus inspired by the experience of the past no less than by the break-through and excitement of the present, let us preserve our humility but dispel our anxiety for the present at least and settle down to enjoy during the next two days the hospitality of our Newcastle friends and to promote as far as we can by this Symposium, the welfare of mankind.

J. D. ALLAN,
President of the Society.

CLINICAL CONSIDERATIONS IN THE CLASSIFICATION AND DIFFERENTIAL DIAGNOSIS OF MUSCULAR DYSTROPHY

JOHN N. WALTON

IT IS reasonable that muscular dystrophy and related disorders should be considered in a symposium devoted to inborn errors of metabolism. While exact knowledge concerning the aetiology and pathogenesis of the muscular dystrophies still eludes us, it is plain that each one of this group of disorders is genetically-determined and it is widely assumed, though far from proved, that a biochemical disorder, possibly in the nature of one or more enzyme defects, may well be responsible for the progressive muscular weakness and wasting which occurs in these conditions. It is not in my terms of reference to consider any of the evidence which is gradually accumulating to implicate a biochemical cause for the muscular dystrophies and this will be considered by Dr. Pennington in the next presentation. It is my brief to consider the clinical characteristics of the various forms of muscular dystrophy, their mode of inheritance and their inter-relationships in order to outline a clinical background to the more fundamental discussions which follow.

The term 'mopathy' may be used to define any disease or syndrome in which the patient's symptoms and/or physical signs can be attributed to pathological, biochemical or electrical changes which are occurring in the muscle fibres or in the interstitial tissues of the voluntary musculature and in which there is no evidence that the symptoms related to the muscular system are in any way secondary to disordered function of the central or peripheral nervous system (Walton, 1966). Within this group we include many degenerative disorders which appear to be genetically-determined as well as others of a primarily biochemical nature and yet others in which the disease process appears to be essentially one of inflammation.

PROGRESSIVE MUSCULAR DYSTROPHY

In this group of disorders, pathological and other evidence seems clearly to indicate that the disease is primarily one of the muscle cell and the process is at present classified as being degenerative in type as there is no evidence available to indicate its fundamental nature. I have therefore defined this disorder elsewhere (Walton, 1960, 1963, 1964a, 1964b, 1965a, 1965b, 1966) as genetically-determined primary degenerative myopathy, but this definition can no longer be regarded as being entirely satisfactory as it is now plain that there are a number of other relatively specific myopathic disorders, which I shall mention briefly below, which are

B   1 genetically-determined but which are not normally regarded as being muscular dystrophies. Central core disease and nemaline myopathy (*vide infra*) are two such disorders.

Classification

Traditionally the muscular dystrophies have been divided into the pseudo-hypertrophic (Duchenne, 1868; Gowers, 1879), pelvic girdle atrophic (Leyden, 1876; Möbius, 1879), facioscapulohumeral (Landouzy & Dejerine, 1884), juvenile scapulohumeral (Erb, 1884), distal (Gowers, 1902; Spiller, 1907), ocular (Hutchinson, 1879; Fuchs, 1890) and congenital (Batten, 1909) varieties. Muscular dystrophy developing in late life was subsequently described by Nevin (1936) but it now seems likely that many patients previously diagnosed as suffering from Nevin's late-life dystrophy are, in fact, examples of polymyositis (Walton & Adams, 1958). We must now accept that the ocular, distal and congenital forms of the disease, though comparatively rare, are to be regarded as distinctive entities, and indeed in Sweden (Welander, 1951, 1957) the distal variety is not uncommon. There remain the pseudohypertrophic, pelvic girdle atrophic, facioscapulohumeral and juvenile scapulohumeral forms into which most cases of muscular dystrophy have previously been classified. As I have pointed out on a number of occasions (Walton, 1966) it has become clear in recent years that this purely clinico-anatomical classification is not satisfactory from either the clinical or genetic standpoint, since if, for instance, one classifies all cases showing pseudohypertrophy into one group, then this is shown to be heterogeneous with several different forms of inheritance and little clinical uniformity. Important contributions have been made to the subject by Tyler & Wintrobe (1950), Stevenson (1953), Becker (1953, 1957), Walton & Nattrass (1954), Lamy & de Grouchy (1954), Walton (1955, 1956a), Kloepfer & Talley (1958), Morton & Chung (1959), Chung & Morton (1959), Blyth & Pugh (1959) and Dubowitz (1960). In 1966 I suggested that the most satisfactory classification of the muscular dystrophies on clinical and genetic grounds was as follows:

1. Duchenne-type muscular dystrophy.
   Sex-linked recessive variety (*a*) Severe; (*b*) Benign.
   Autosomal recessive variety.
2. Limb-girdle muscular dystrophy.
   Autosomal recessive.
   Sporadic.
3. Facioscapulohumeral muscular dystrophy.
   Autosomal dominant.
4. Distal muscular dystrophy.
5. Ocular myopathy, including oculopharyngeal.
6. Congenital muscular dystrophy.

This classification, being based essentially on clinical criteria as originally proposed by Walton & Nattrass (1954), can still be justly criticised and others (Becker, 1957) would prefer a classification based purely upon genetic grounds. Thus Becker would prefer to reserve the eponymous term 'Duchenne' for the severe sex-linked recessive cases of early onset and comparatively rapid progression and would classify the more benign X-linked cases of later onset, which I have included in the group of Duchenne type dystrophy, as a different disease. All authors are agreed concerning the consistent clinical pattern and autosomal dominant inheritance of facioscapulohumeral muscular dystrophy, but the noso-logical status of the limb-girdle type is much less clear-cut. It is, for instance, doubtful whether cases of early onset with pelvic girdle weakness, which resemble clinically other cases of the Duchenne type dystrophy but which may occur in both sexes and run a comparatively benign course, should be classified as a benign autosomal recessive sub-group of the Duchenne type, as I have done, or in the category of so-called limb-girdle muscular dys-trophy. Thus classification will clearly prove to be a fertile source of controversy for some years to come and it is plain that many more detailed family studies in numerous countries using rigid clinical and genetic criteria will be necessary before a final and definitive answer to the problem can be given. For the present, however, the classification given above is a reasonably satisfactory guide to prognosis and to genetic counselling, which is the major justification of any form of classification.

Clinical features

As will be evident, the clinical manifestations of muscular dystrophy must depend upon the pattern of muscular involvement and upon the rate of development of muscular weakness and wasting. Weakness in the muscles of the pelvic girdle gives rise to a waddling gait with accentuation of the lumbar lordosis, a protuberant abdomen, a tendency to fall, difficulty in climbing stairs and in rising from the floor or from a low chair. The affected individual will climb up his legs when rising from the floor (Gowers' sign). Weakness in the shoulder girdle gives an unusually sloping appearance of the shoulders and the scapulae will rise prominently when the patient attempts to abduct the arms. Affected individuals have difficulty in lifting their arms above the head and commonly use trick movements, placing one hand beneath the opposite elbow in order to elevate an arm. Facial weakness causes inability to close the eyes, to whistle and to pout the lips, while distal weakness will give impairment of grip and of fine finger move-ments and foot-drop. Contractures commonly occur as the disease advances and result either from weakness developing in a group of muscles while its antagonists remain comparatively powerful, or from postural changes resulting from, say, a wheelchair existence. Differential diagnosis will be considered below, but it may be mentioned at this stage that one of the most important clinical characteristics of all forms of muscular dystrophy is that of selectivity of muscle involvement. Thus in the upper limbs, for instance, it is common to find that the serrati and pectoral muscles are weak and atrophic, as are biceps and brachioradialis, when deltoid and triceps remain relatively powerful. In the lower limbs, quadriceps and anterior tibials tend to be particularly weakened early in the disease and the calf muscles are spared, but there are some cases of limb-girdle muscular dystrophy in which the hamstrings and quadriceps are affected equally. Nevertheless, this selective pattern of involvement of proximal muscles in many of the forms of muscular dystrophy is a most useful guide to differential diagnosis as it is uncommon to find such a pattern in other forms of myopathy.

The Duchenne Type Muscular Dystrophy

As this condition is almost invariably due to a sex-linked recessive gene, 95 per cent or more of the cases occur in males, but the small number of affected females can be accounted for by the occasional families in which this form of the disease is inherited by an autosomal recessive mechanism; as already mentioned above, it is not certain whether these cases are correctly classified within this group or whether they more properly belong in the limb-girdle group. I can only say that there do exist a small number of cases in girls whose pattern of muscular involvement and clinical course is, apart from its comparative benignity, in other respects very like that of the Duchenne type. Evidence in favour of sex-linked recessive inheritance in most families, however, comes first from the inspection of pedigrees (Walton, 1955), secondly from the fact that several women have been known to have affected children by more than one male (Walton, 1955), thirdly from the finding of families in which there is crossing-over with colour blindness (Philip, Walton & Smith, 1956; Emery, 1966) and fourthly from the fact that two cases of the disease have been reported in patients of female morphology suffering from Turner's syndrome (ovarian agenesis) with an XO chromosome constitution (Walton, 1956a; Ferrier, Bamatter & Klein, 1965). In the severe sex-linked group, which accounts for 80 per cent of all cases, the disease usually begins in the first three years of life, but in about 10 per cent of the sex-linked cases the condition is much more benign and of later onset, beginning usually in the second decade but occasionally as late as the third.

In all cases of this type, the pelvic girdle muscles are first affected and the shoulder girdles are involved later. Enlargement of the calf muscles, but sometimes of quadriceps, deltoids and other muscles as well, occurs in about 90 per cent of cases at some stage but later disappears as the disease advances. In most patients there is steady and rapid progression leading as a rule to inability to walk within 6 to 10 years of the onset, but many patients in the mild sex-linked recessive and autosomal recessive sub-groups continue to walk into early adult life. False or apparent clinical improvement may sometimes occur between the ages of 5 and 8 years when the rate of deterioration due to the disease is apparently outstripped by the processes of normal physical development. Once the child is confined to a wheelchair, progressive deformity with muscular contractures, skeletal distortion and atrophy occur and death usually results from inanition, respiratory infection or cardiac failure towards the end of the second decade. Associated clinical features in these cases, including evidence of intellectual backwardness and of cardiac involvement, have been reviewed by Walton (1966).

Carrier detection

In the past few years there have been considerable advances in methods of recognising those female carriers who are likely to pass on the gene responsible for the severe sex-linked recessive variety of the disease; it is less certain whether these methods are as accurate in the benign sex-linked families. This information is of great value in genetic counselling as any proven carrier will transmit the disease to half her sons, and half her daughters will themselves be carriers. Attempts in the past using estimations of creatine and creatinine excretion and of serum aldolase activity (Leyburn, Thomson & Walton, 1961; Chung, Morton & Peters, 1960; Schapira, Dreyfus, Schapira & Demos, 1960; Dreyfus & Schapira, 1962) were somewhat disappointing, as was measurement of limb-to-limb circulation time (Schapira, Dreyfus, Schapira & Demos, 1960). Recently, however, estimation of the serum creatine kinase has proved to be much more useful (Hughes, 1962; Richterich, Rosin, Aebi & Rossi, 1963; Pearce, Pennington & Walton, 1964) and we have found that in about two-thirds of female carriers the serum creatine kinase activity is consistently raised. Physical exercise, suggested as a possible provocative test for increasing enzyme activity in carriers (Stephens & Lewin, 1965) has not in our hands proved to be helpful (Hudgson, Gardner-Medwin, Pennington & Walton, 1967). Wilson, Evans & Carter (1965) have shown that if enzyme activity is charted on a logarithmic scale, approximately 90 per cent of the female carriers of both the severe and benign sex-linked recessive varieties of the disease can probably be identified by this method. However, Emery (1965a) found that he could only detect about 65 per cent of carriers of the severe Duchenne type and approximately 20 per cent of carriers of the benign X-linked variety using serum creatine kinase activity alone. Attempts have more recently been made to identify carriers by electrophysiological means. Van den Bosch (1963) and Barwick (1963) both found minimal electromyographic abnormalities resembling those of muscular dystrophy in some female carriers, but Davey & Woolf (1965) and Caruso & Buchthal

(1965) found that they could identify relatively few carriers with this method. On the other hand, Hausmanowa-Petrusewicz *et al.* (1965) found increased polyphasic potentials and electrocardiographic abnormalities in a substantial proportion of carriers, and Willison (1965) reported that an electronic spike-counting method of analysing the electromyogram may prove to be of value. More recently, Gardner-Medwin (1968) has found that measurement of mean action potential duration in the electromyogram is a more hopeful method of carrier detection than was at one time suggested. Finally, it is also apparent that muscle biopsy sections obtained from carriers may show significant pathological changes (Dubowitz, 1963; Walton, 1964a; Stephens & Lewin, 1965; Emery, 1963, 1965b) and Emery (1965a, 1965c) has found a pattern of lactic dehydrogenase isoenzymes in such material similar to that observed in established cases of muscular dystrophy. The present position seems to be that approximately two-thirds of female carriers can be detected utilising serum creatine kinase estimation alone. Probably up to one-half of the remainder can be identified by means of electromyographic methods at present available and/or muscle biopsy, but there remain a small number of women known to be definite carriers on genetic grounds in whom the results of all of these investigations are normal. Hence positive abnormalities in a putative carrier are of value for genetic counselling, but negative results are less certain and it is still not possible completely to reassure a young woman who presents herself for these tests that if they are all negative there is no chance of her having a dystrophic child.

Limb-Girdle Muscular Dystrophy

This variety of muscular dystrophy occurs equally in the two sexes and usually begins in the second or third decade of life, but occasionally the onset is delayed until middle life. Usually the disease is inherited by an autosomal recessive mechanism (Walton, 1955, 1956a) but many cases are sporadic and may well be due to manifestation in the heterozygote (Morton & Chung, 1959; Chung & Morton, 1959). In about half the cases muscle weakness begins in the shoulder girdle muscles and may remain limited to these for many years before later spreading to involve the pelvic girdle. In the other half, by contrast, the pelvic girdle muscles are first involved and as a rule the shoulder girdle muscles are subsequently affected within 10 years. Enlargement or pseudohypertrophy of the calf muscles is not uncommon in these cases and sometimes involves other groups. The severity of this form of the disease and its rate of progression varies a good deal from case to case and from family to family. In many cases weakness and wasting are asymmetrical initially and sometimes there is apparent arrest of the muscle weakness for a year or more, but in most cases disability becomes severe within 20 years of the onset. Contractures and skeletal deformity occur late in the course of the disease but progress more rapidly when the patient is unable to walk. Most sufferers become severely disabled in middle life and many die before the normal age. The prognosis is generally better in those cases in which the shoulder girdle muscles are first involved, but this rule is not invariable.

Facioscapulohumeral Muscular Dystrophy

This variety also occurs equally in the two sexes and may begin at any age from childhood until adult life, though most often it is first recognised in adolescence. Inheritance is by an autosomal dominant mechanism (Stevenson, 1953; Becker, 1953; Walton, 1955, 1956a, Morton & Chung, 1959) though some families show apparent sex-limitation. There are families on record in which the pattern of inheritance has suggested an autosomal recessive mechanism, but these are uncommon. Usually facial involvement occurs first and is always found early. It is accompanied by involvement of the shoulder girdle muscles, winging of the scapulae, weakness of the pectorals, involvement of the biceps and brachioradiales and difficulty in raising the arms above the head. Muscular enlargement or pseudohypertrophy is relatively uncommon but is occasionally seen in the calves and elsewhere, particularly in the deltoids. Many cases show selective involvement of the anterior tibial muscles with bilateral foot-drop in the lower extremities, and some few in whom the disease progresses unusually rapidly develop a particularly severe accentuation of the lumbar lordosis at a comparatively early stage. Usually, however, the condition is very benign, runs a course with prolonged periods of apparent arrest and muscular contractures and skeletal deformity are rare. There are many patients in whom the disease is apparently abortive and after certain muscles become weak and atrophic, it shows no further progression. The facial appearance is particularly characteristic. The face is often unlined, wrinkles are missing and there is a typical pouting appearance of the lips with a characteristic transverse smile. Affected individuals cannot close the eyes and cannot bury their eyelashes on command, while few can retain air under pressure in the mouth. Most patients with this condition survive and remain active until the normal age.

Distal Muscular Dystrophy

In recent years Welander (1951, 1957, 1966) has reported her experience with over 250 cases of this form of muscular dystrophy, which in Sweden is inherited as a dominant character, begins usually between the ages of 40 and 60 and affects both sexes, though it is commoner in men than in women. Usually the small muscles of the hands are first affected and the weakness gradually spreads proximally. In the legs, the anterior tibial muscles and calves waste first, though later proximal muscles are involved, in contrast to the pattern of weakness which obtains in peroneal muscular atrophy, in which disease the condition remains limited to the distal parts of the limbs. The Swedish type of distal myopathy is a comparatively benign and slowly progressive disorder. In other parts of the world distal muscular dystrophy is rare. When it does occur, it usually does so sporadically, tends to begin in younger patients and on the whole shows more rapid progress and more rapidly increasing disability (Barnes, 1932; Milhorat & Wolff, 1943). The condition which Biemond (1955, 1966) has entitled 'myopathia distalis juvenilis hereditaria' is believed by many not to be a myopathy but to be a variant of peroneal muscular atrophy (Charcot-Marie-Tooth disease).

Ocular Myopathy

Muscular dystrophy of the external ocular muscles (Hutchinson, 1879; Fuchs, 1890; Kiloh & Nevin, 1951) usually begins with progressive bilateral ptosis. Diplopia is rare and in most cases slowly progressive bilateral external ophthalmoplegia develops over a period of some years. Usually there is also some weakness in the upper facial muscles and in many patients there is subsequent slight weakness and atrophy of neck and girdle muscles in the extremities. The facial weakness is particularly severe in the orbicularis oculi and is less severe than in facioscapulohumeral muscular dystrophy. This variety of the disease is sometimes seen in patients with disorders of the hereditary ataxia group and in some of them pigmentary retinal degeneration is seen (Walsh, 1957; Erdbrink, 1957; Walton, 1964b). Even in cases of this type, in which it has often been assumed in the past that the ophthalmoplegia might be due to degeneration in the oculo-motor nuclei, histological examination has usually demonstrated that the affliction of the ocular muscles is myopathic. Until recently I had assumed that the dysphagia which has been noted in a number of these cases was a common variant of the disease process, but in 1962 Victor, Hayes & Adams included cases with dysphagia in a separate group which they entitled 'oculopharyngeal muscular dystrophy). More recently, in a comprehensive review, Bray, Kaarsoo & Ross (1965) have shown that there are essential differences between classical ocular myopathy and the oculopharyngeal variety. In particular they found that in patients with dysphagia the mean age of onset of symptoms was 40 years, but in patients without dysphagia it was 23 years. Barbeau (1965, 1966) has recently shown that most of the patients with oculopharyngeal muscular dystrophy reported from several centres appear to be descendants of a single French-Canadian family which he has investigated in detail. Thus there seems to be some justification for regarding oculopharyngeal muscular dystrophy of late onset as a separate disorder, though it is probably closely related to the more common form of ocular myopathy which usually develops first in early adult life. On the whole the genetic pattern in these families is one of autosomal dominant inheritance and this is particularly true of the oculopharyngeal variety. Many cases of ocular myopathy without pharyngeal involvement appear to be sporadic, but in other families there is evidence of either autosomal recessive or autosomal dominant inheritance (Kiloh & Nevin, 1951).

Congenital Muscular Dystrophy

It was Batten who in 1909 suggested that the syndrome of amyotonia congenita, as first described by Oppenheim (1900) might be due to a simple atrophic myopathy of congenital origin. In 1909 Silvestri described two sibs who were hypotonic from birth and one of whom, at the age of 6 years, had widespread muscular weakness and wasting suggestive of a limb-girdle type of muscular dystrophy. In 1937, de Lange studied a family of infants with congenital hypotonia, in each of which muscular weakness was rapidly progressive and the affected individuals died within 3 months of birth. In one of these infants pathological changes were found in the muscle suggestive of a muscular dystrophy. Banker, Victor & Adams (1957) described two sibs, one of whom showed widespread muscular weakness and multiple contractures present from birth and the clinical picture was one of arthrogryposis multiplex congenita. In this case, too, histological examination of muscle samples showed changes which were clearly those of a dystrophic process. Short (1963) reported another such case with post-mortem findings, and Gubbay, Walton & Pearce (1966) have recently described detailed clinical and pathological studies of such a case in a child of 4 years. The nosological status of this disorder is still indefinite. It is plain that there are a group of cases in which muscular weakness is present from birth, with or without contractures suggesting arthrogryposis, and in these patients histological examination of the muscle reveals unquestionable dystrophic changes. It seems that in a few patients in this category the disease is rapidly progressive and death occurs within the first year of life, but there remain a number of the reported cases in which the disease process has seemed to be somewhat non-progressive over a period of several years in that the children, though unable to stand or walk, have not deteriorated. Many more cases of this type will need to be reported and analysed before the exact nature of this illness and its relation to the other forms of muscular dystrophy can be clarified.

DISORDERS WITH MYOTONIA

Myotonia, which occurs not only in man but also in certain goats (Brown & Harvey, 1939) is a phenomenon of continued active contraction of a muscle which persists after voluntary innervation ceases. An electrical after-discharge in the electromyogram can be seen to accompany the phenomenon. Not all conditions in which myotonia is observed are muscular dystrophies, but in one at least of the hereditary syndromes in which myotonia is a well-recognised phenomenon, namely dystrophia myotonica, there are dystrophic changes in the muscles and hence this group of disorders deserves brief mention. Three hereditary syndromes, all with autosomal dominant inheritance, have been described, namely myotonia congenita, dystrophia myotonica and paramyotonia congenita. The clinical features of each may vary considerably so that not only are transitional cases seen, but very occasionally a single family will be found to contain examples of two of the syndromes in any of the possible combinations. These views have led to controvery over whether the syndromes are merely different manifestations of the same condition, a view put forward by Maas & Paterson (1939, 1950). The great difference between the course and prognosis of typical cases of dystrophia myotonica and of myotonia congenita, however, and the fact that in the vast majority of families the conditions breed true suggest that for the present they should be regarded as different diseases. The evidence on this question has been reviewed recently by Caughey & Myrianthopoulos (1963). Further nosological problems arise over the close relationship of paramyotonia with the periodic paralyses. It seems clear that all of these disorders are more closely related to each other than they are to the pure muscular dystrophies.

Myotonia Congenita

Myotonia congenita (Thomsen, 1876; Nissen, 1923; Thomasen, 1948) usually begins at birth but symptoms may be delayed until the end of the first or even into the second decade. The myotonia is generally widespread and may not only affect grip and ocular movements, but characteristically causes a generalized painless stiffness which is accentuated by rest and cold and gradually relieved by exercise. There is typically diffuse hypertrophy of muscles which usually persists throughout life, although the myotonia tends gradually to diminish. Affected infants may have a curiously strangled cry and some difficulty in feeding. Rarely myotonia may increase during exertion (myotonia paradoxa) when it must be distinguished from the cramping stiffness of McArdle's disease. Hypertrophia musculorum vera (Friedrich, 1863; Spiller, 1913) may be a variant of myotonia congenita.

Dystrophia Myotonica

Dystrophia myotonica (myotonia atrophica) was described by Steinert (1909) and Batten & Gibb (1909) and has been reviewed by Thomasen (1948) and Caughey & Myrianthopoulos (1963). It is a diffuse systemic disorder in which myotonia and muscular atrophy are accompanied by cataracts, frontal baldness in the male, gonadal atrophy, cardiomyopathy, impaired pulmonary ventilation, mild endocrine anomalies, bone changes, mental defect or dementia and abnormalities of the serum immunoglobulins. Association with other congenital disorders is common (Caughey & Myrianthopoulos, 1963; Pruzanski, 1966), the inheritance is autosomal and dominant and affected families show progressive social decline in successive generations, diminished fertility, an increased infantile mortality rate and a high incidence of mental backwardness. The impression is often gained that the disease increases in severity and becomes earlier in onset in successive generations, but Penrose (1947) has argued that this is an artefact of ascertainment. It is also uncertain whether cataracts occurring in late life in earlier generations without muscle disease are really manifestations of the disorder.

The presenting symptoms of the disorder are usually weakness in the hands, difficulty in walking and a tendency to fall, but some patients do in fact observe that they are unable to let go of objects as a result of myotonia. Poor vision, loss of weight, impotence or loss of libido, ptosis and increased sweating are common. The condition usually begins between the ages of 20 and 50, but detectable clinical features of the disorder are often present in the second decade. Rarely the disease presents as hypotonia with facial weakness and feeding difficulties in infancy (Vanier, 1960; Dodge, Gamstorp, Byers & Russell, 1965; Pruzanski, 1966).

The facial appearance is characteristic, ptosis is almost invariable and there is often symmetrical impairment of ocular movement. There is difficulty in closing the eyes, in retracting the corner of the mouth and in pursing the lips, and often the lower lid droops. Wasting of the masseters, temporal muscles and sternomastoids gives a characteristic haggard appearance, while the jaw sags and the head hangs forward because of muscular weakness. Dysarthria due to weakness of the facial muscles or myotonia of the tongue is common, weakness and wasting in the limbs affects mainly the muscles of the forearms, the anterior tibial group and the calves and peronei; this is distinct from the proximal weakness of the other common muscular dystrophies. Later more proximal and more distal limb muscles are involved. Myotonia is often limited to the tongue, forearm and hand, but it may be generalized; it tends to become less apparent as the disease progresses. The tendon reflexes are reduced in the affected muscles and contractures occur in the late stages. Slit-lamp examination reveals cataracts in about 90 per cent of cases. Cardiac involvement is common and the pulmonary vital capacity and especially the maximum expiratory pressure are often impaired. Disordered oesophageal contraction can be demonstrated by contrast radiography or manometry. The testes are usually small, their histology resembling that of Klinefelter's syndrome though the nuclear sex is male. Females may have irregular menstruation and infertility and parturition may be prolonged in fully-developed cases. Pituitary function is usually normal but there is often a selective failure of adrenal androgenic function and occasionally thyroid activity and glucose utilization are impaired (Marshall, 1959; Caughey & Myrianthopoulos, 1963). Hyperostosis of the skull vault, localized or diffuse, and a small sella turcica are frequent radiological findings (Jequier, 1950; Caughey, 1952; Walton & Warrick, 1954). Both mental defect and progressive dementia occur. Only 24 of Thomasen's (1948) 101 cases were of normal intelligence. Rosman & Kakulas (1966) have described neuronal heterotopias at autopsy in 4 cases, of whom 3 were mentally defective, and investigation in life may reveal EEG abnormalities (Barwick, Osselton & Walton, 1965) or cerebral ventricular enlargement (Refsum, Lounum, Sjaastad & Engeset, 1967). Excessive catabolism of immunoglobulin-G has been demonstrated in this disorder by Wochner, Drews, Strober & Waldmann (1966).

The course is one of steady deterioration in that most patients are severely disabled and unable to walk within 15-20 years of the onset. Death occurs before the normal age, usually from chest infection or cardiac failure and these patients are particularly at risk during anaesthesia because of impaired ventilation or possibly because of increased sensitivity to thiopentone (Caughey & Myrianthopoulos, 1963; Gillam, Heaf, Kaufman & Lucas, 1964).

Paramyotonia Congenita

This condition was first described by Eulenburg (1886). In the families he described the affected individuals suffered from myotonia which was apparent only on exposure to cold, and in addition the patients experienced attacks of unexplained generalized muscular weakness. It is now well recognized that these attacks are similar to those of familial periodic paralysis and that in most cases this is of the hyperkalaemic variety (Gamstorp, 1956). Although the nosological status of paramyotonia congenita is confused and its exact relationship to the periodic paralyses is still uncertain, it remains a useful diagnostic category.

DIFFERENTIAL DIAGNOSIS

The differential diagnosis of the myopathies depends first upon clinical history and examination, secondly upon electromyographic and other neuro-physiological evidence, thirdly upon biochemical findings and fourthly upon pathological changes in muscle as revealed by biopsy.

Clinical Diagnosis

In the characteristic case of muscular dystrophy showing the usual slowly progressive pattern of increasing muscular weakness and selective atrophy of the proximal limb muscles, diagnosis is rarely in doubt. On the other hand, in an infant or young child showing a picture of relatively diffuse non-progressive atrophy and weakness of skeletal muscles which superficially resembles muscular dystrophy, full investigation may demonstrate that the condition belongs to one of the group of so-called benign congenital or non-progressive myopathies. There are indeed a group of cases of so-called benign congenital myopathy and hypotonia in which the nature of the disease process remains uncertain. In 1958 Krabbe described such a case under the title of 'congenital universal muscular hypoplasia' and similar cases have been described by Ford (1960) and Fukuyama, Yamada & Kawazura (1961). Turner (1940), 1949) described 6 members of one family who presented as floppy infants but who later improved and were able to walk at about the age of 5 years. A 50-year follow-up of the survivors of this family (Turner & Lees, 1962) showed that the muscular disorder was static and non-progressive.

A similar non-progressive myopathy in adults, present from birth and showing myasthenic features responsive to prostigmine has been described by Rowland & Eskenazi (1956) and Walton, Geschwind & Simpson (1956). Walton (1956b, 1957) also pointed out that of a number of infants who were hypotonic at birth and in whom spinal muscular atrophy and other recognized causes of infantile hypotonia had been excluded, some recovered completely and corresponded to Oppenheim's (1900) description of amyotonia congenita, whereas others showed persisting weakness, hypotonia and hyper-mobility of joints extending into later childhood and even sometimes into adult life. Paine (1963) has had a similar experience.

The first specific form of benign congenital myopathy was reported in 1956 by Shy & Magee. They described a family of children who did not walk until about the age of 4 years. The patients showed profound and widespread muscular hypotonia and muscle biopsy revealed large muscle fibres with central cores which had different staining properties from other fibrils. Further cases have been described by Engel, Foster, Hughes, Huxley & Mahler (1961) and by Bethlem & Meyjes (1960). Dubowitz & Pearse (1960) found the central core to be devoid of oxidative enzymes and of phosphorylase activity and suggested that it was non-functioning.

Shy and his colleagues (1963) described another congenital non-progressive myopathy in which curious collections of rod-shaped bodies were found within the muscle fibres. It is now apparent that in many such cases the clinical diagnosis can be suspected as these patients show not only evidence of a diffuse myopathy, but also as a rule facial weakness, a high arched palate, prognathism of the lower jaw and skeletal changes resembling those of arachnodactyly, though none of the other stigmata of Marfan's syndrome are present (Conen, Murphy & Donohue, 1963; Engel, Wanko & Fenichel, 1964; Ford, 1960). Examination of muscle from such cases with the electron microscope (Price, Gordon, Pearson, Munsat & Blumberg, 1965; Hudgson, Gardner-Medwin, Fulthorpe & Walton, 1967) has shown that the sub-sarcolemmal rods appear to be due to a selective swelling and degeneration of Z-bands with consequent destruction of myofilaments in the adjacent part of the muscle fibre.

More recently still, in similar floppy infants showing a picture of non-progressive myopathic weakness, one group have shown giant abnormal mitochondria only visible on examination of muscle under the electron microscope (Shy & Gonatas, 1964; Shy, Gonatas & Perez, (1966).

Yet another new myopathy has now been described which may give some insight into maturation of the muscle cell and may represent the first example of cellular arrest. This condition, entitled by Spiro, Shy & Gonatas (1966) 'myotubular myopathy', was found in a 9-year-old child with a form of Mobius disease characterized by facial diplegia, external ocular palsies, a decrease in muscle mass, moderate symmetrical muscle weakness and poor development of all somatic muscles.

Thus gradually a number of new syndromes giving rise to the picture of benign congenital or relatively non-progressive myopathy are being described and must be distinguished from the larger group of cases of progressive muscular dystrophy. Yet another such, to which Dr. Hudgson will be referring later in this symposium, is skeletal muscle glycogenosis due to acid maltase deficiency, which in our recent experience gave a clinical picture not dissimilar from that of muscular dystrophy in an adolescent girl and an adult woman.

If the pattern of muscular weakness and wasting is somewhat obscured by subcutaneous fat or when muscular involvement is predominantly distal, as in dystrophia myotonica and distal myopathy, it may not always be easy to distinguish muscular dystrophy from neuropathic disorders such as progressive muscular atrophy, motor neurone disease, polyneuropathy and peroneal muscular atrophy. Usually, however, the associated neurological signs and in particular the sensory abnormalities which generally occur in polyneuropathy and peroneal muscular atrophy are sufficient to clarify the condition. However, one condition which is often wrongly diagnosed as muscular dystrophy, particularly in the early stages, is the so-called pseudomyopathic form of spinal muscular atrophy or the Kugelberg-Welander syndrome. This condition, which is inherited by an autosomal recessive gene, can affect more than one member of a family and not uncommonly begins in childhood and adolescence (Kugelberg & Welander, 1956). This condition tends to be very much more variable in its clinical presentation and particularly in the pattern of muscular involvement than does muscular dystrophy, and in differentiating it from the various myopathies electromyography is of particular value, since in this spinal disorder the classical features of central denervation atrophy are almost always found. In a recent review of 18 cases, Gardner-Medwin, Hudgson & Walton (1967) have pointed out that many of the patients they have examined had previously been diagnosed as examples of muscular dystrophy. They give reasons for suggesting that this is not an independent disease entity but that it is probably no more than a benign variant of infantile spinal muscular atrophy (Werdnig-Hoffmann disease).

While it is usually comparatively easy to distinguish myopathy from neuropathy on clinical grounds alone, it is often much more difficult to separate cases of sporadic muscular dystrophy from other forms of myopathy. Difficulty in distinguishing the disorder from the various congenital myopathies has already been mentioned. The possibility of an endocrine cause for muscle weakness must always be given consideration and such conditions as thyrotoxicosis, Cushing's syndrome, Addison's disease and metabolic bone disease should always be borne in mind. Furthermore, it must be appreciated that in untreated myasthenia gravis fatiguability of muscles may not always be immediately apparent and in any patient with proximal muscle weakness of comparatively recent onset, even if there is sparing of the ocular and bulbar muscles, a diagnostic injection of edrophonium hydrochloride is indicated. Occasional improvement after such an injection is seen in cases of polymyositis and in the myasthenic-myopathic syndrome complicating bronchogenic carcinoma. It should also be remembered that in some cases of periodic paralysis, permanent muscular atrophy may eventually supervene, though usually in such cases there is clear-cut history of episodic attacks of weakness which must then be elucidated by biochemical methods.

I do not propose to discuss in detail the differential diagnosis between muscular dystrophy and subacute or chronic polymyositis, as I have given elsewhere (Walton, 1964a, 1964b, 1966) some criteria which are of value in making the distinction. The most important points are first the rapidity of onset and occasional remissions which occur in polymyositis; secondly the global weakness and wasting, unlike the selective pattern of muscular involvement of muscular dystrophy, which occurs in polymyositis; thirdly the importance of a positive family history; fourthly the almost constant involvement of neck muscles and the frequent occurrence of dysphagia, which strongly favour a diagnosis of polymyositis; finally, associated phenomena such as skin changes, subcutaneous calcification and the Raynaud phenomenon are found in a considerable number of cases of polymyositis. Even with the help of these and other clinical guides, there are nevertheless cases in which the clinical diagnosis remains in doubt and must then depend upon a combination of clinical, electromyographic, biochemical and histological findings.

Electrophysiological Diagnosis

The electromyogram is of particular value in distinguishing between muscular wasting of neuropathic and myopathic origin. Kugelberg in 1949 showed that in muscular dystrophy the electromyogram demonstrated an excessive proportion of polyphasic and short-duration potentials of low amplitude, and in 1952 Walton pointed out that a method of automatic frequency analysis of the electromyogram was of some value in diagnosing myopathic change. Buchthal, Rosenfalck & Erminio (1960) showed that the motor unit action potentials recorded during volitional activity in dystrophic individuals showed a decrease in the mean action potential duration and voltage which resulted from reduced motor unit territory and fibre density caused by patchy degeneration of muscle fibres. These changes were invariably observed in established cases of muscular dystrophy of the Duchenne type, but in some of the more benign forms of muscular dystrophy, such as the limb-girdle and facioscapulohumeral varieties, the mean motor unit potential durations fell within the normal range (Buchthal, 1962). Nevertheless, even in these more benign forms of dystrophy Buchthal found a greatly increased proportion of polyphasic potentials exceeding the normal 3-4 per cent. He also found, in collaboration with Farmer and Rosenfalck (Farmer, Buchthal & Rosenfalck, 1959) that the absolute refractory period of voluntary muscle was reduced in most patients with muscular dystrophy. Unfortunately, however, although the electromyogram is thus of great value in diagnosing myopathic change, it cannot be used with the same degree of certainty to distinguish between muscular dystrophy and polymyositis as the pattern of volitional activity seen in the two diseases is similar (Buchthal & Pinelli, 1953). It is true that in polymyositis more spontaneous activity in the form of fibrillation potentials and positive potentials as well as pseudomyotonic discharges may be recorded (Walton & Adams, 1958) but this activity occurring spontaneously is by no means diagnostic and similar changes are seen in a proportion of patients with muscular dystrophy; we have found them to be prominent in skeletal muscle glycogenosis. In patients with myotonia, a more characteristic type of discharge, taking the form of chains of oscillations of high frequency, is seen, but similar spontaneous discharges evoked by movement of the exploring electrode are occasionally recorded from various forms of non-myotonic myopathy, particularly polymyositis. Changes in the motor unit action potentials similar to those observed in muscular dystrophy are found in thyrotoxic myopathy (Ramsay, 1965; Sanderson & Adey, 1952; Havard, Campbell, Ross & Spence, 1963) and in steroid myopathy (Müller & Kugelberg, 1959; Williams, 1959; Coomes, 1965) as well as in the myopathies of Addison's disease and sarcoidosis (Buchthal, 1962).

In myasthenia gravis the electromyogram may be entirely normal, except that a myopathic pattern as described above may be obtained from a fatigued muscle. However, the recording of action potentials obtained in response to supramaximal stimulation of the motor nerve is a useful technique in diagnosing myasthenia in some cases and in distinguishing this condition from the myasthenic-myopathic syndrome complicating bronchogenic carcinoma.

Biochemical Diagnosis

I do not propose to consider the various biochemical tests which can be employed in differentiating between the various forms of myopathy in detail, as these will be dealt with by Dr. Pennington. For many years the only biochemical test in common use in diagnosing muscular dystrophy was the estimation of creatine and creatinine in the urine, but it soon became apparent that this finding was relatively non-specific as a similar creatinuria could be found in patients with neuropathic atrophy and in some suffering from a variety of other diseases. Considerable specificity has been given to the biochemical diagnosis of muscular dystrophy with the aid of serum enzyme estimations and there can be little doubt that the estimation of the serum creatine kinase is now the single most useful diagnostic test for muscular dystrophy, particularly of the Duchenne type. The rise in the serum activity of this enzyme in such cases is far greater than that seen in virtually any other condition with the single exception of acute and severe polymyositis.

It only remains to be mentioned that there are a great many other biochemical tests which may sometimes be necessary to distinguish between muscular dystrophy and various other forms of myopathy. For instance, when endocrine myopathy is suspected, a larger number of tests apposite to the diagnosis of the individual endocrine deficiency under consideration may well be required, and the same is true in cases of suspected myopathy due to metabolic bone disease or in patients with suspected periodic paralysis. It is not, however, proposed to discuss these and the many other diagnostic tests which may be occasionally required in any detail.

Pathological Diagnosis

As Erb first pointed out in 1884, the most striking pathological changes observed in dystrophic muscle are first a marked variation in fibre size with swelling of some fibres and marked atrophy of others. In the large hypertrophic fibres it is common to find central nuclei, sometimes lying in chains, and evidence of fibre-splitting is commonly apparent. In addition there is marked infiltration with connective tissue and fat between the damaged muscle fibres. For many years, however, it was not widely recognized that areas of muscle fibre necrosis and phagocytosis are commonly found in all varieties of muscular dystrophy and that evidence of spontaneous though abortive regeneration is not infrequently seen in non-myotonic cases (Pearce & Walton, 1962). This latter type of change, which many authors have felt to be rare in muscular dystrophy but common by contrast in polymyositis, is now known to be a frequent finding in dystrophic patients particularly in the early stages.

Observations on muscle biopsy samples obtained from preclinical cases of muscular dystrophy of the Duchenne type diagnosed within the first few months of life on the basis of serum creatine kinase estimation are of particular interest. Original observations were made by Pearson (1962) and have been confirmed by ourselves (Hudgson, Walton & Pearce, 1967). Not only have such sections shown muscle fibre necrosis and phagocytosis and marked variations in fibre size, but profuse abortive regenerative activity is a particular feature of these muscle sections, suggesting that attempts to repair the process of muscle fibre degeneration are particularly common at this stage of the disease.

It is now well recognized that although it is usually possible on the basis of histological changes observed in the muscle biopsy sample to determine that the patient is suffering from a myopathic as distinct from a neuropathic disorder (the latter group of conditions usually demonstrate characteristic grouped atrophy of muscle fibres, though so-called disseminated neurogenic atrophy, in which groups of small numbers of fibres are atrophic, may be less easy to recognize), yet the distinction between polymyositis and the other non-dystrophic myopathies on the one hand and muscular dystrophy on the other is not always easy. There is a striking degree of overlap of pathological change which may be seen in both diseases. Virtually the only histological criterion which is diagnostic of polymyositis as distinct from muscular dystrophy is massive cellular infiltration, but this is relatively uncommon and an active process of degeneration and phagocytosis of muscle fibres may certainly be seen in both diseases.

It must, however, be mentioned that nowadays we have at our command certain highly-specialized techniques of investigation which have added considerable precision to diagnosis. Two which deserve particular mention are histochemistry and examination of the ultrastructure of muscle fibres using the electron microscope. Without question, electron microscopy has clarified the nature of the structural changes occurring in the muscle in many of the relatively specific congenital myopathies referred to above, but as yet it has given little information concerning aetiology. One must also say that these techniques are still in their infancy and as yet no absolutely specific findings have been demonstrated by the method which are unquestionably helpful in distinguishing between muscular dystrophy and many other forms of myopathy.

Conclusions

It has been possible in this paper to do little more than to mention briefly the clinical characteristics of the more important varieties of human muscular dystrophy and to describe some general principles of diagnosis using clinical and ancillary methods. Undoubtedly modern techniques of clinical and scientific investigation have greatly clarified our knowledge of muscle disease within the last ten to twenty years. In certain instances it has been possible to demonstrate, as Dr. Hudgson will indicate, that a pattern of muscular weakness and wasting may be attributable to a deficiency of a single enzyme causing glycogen storage disease of muscle.

Unfortunately, despite all the investigations carried out on the muscular dystrophies to date, the nature of the primary abnormality within the muscle cell which causes it to degenerate is still obscure. One major difficulty is to determine why it is that certain muscles are selectively involved by the disease process at a time when others are comparatively spared. Many research workers are at present turning their attention to this problem and are comparing not only the normal with the abnormal, but also the behaviour of different muscles in normal patients and in those with muscular dystrophy. I would include myself in the number of those who believe that like many other genetically-determined disorders, muscular dystrophy will eventually prove to be due to a specific disorder of metabolism of the muscle cell or possible of its membrane. When that time comes, then there may perhaps be hope of finding some effective treatment for this disease which, in its severe form, is so tragic in its effects, not only upon the individual sufferer but also upon his family and the community.

REFERENCES

BANKER, B. Q., VICTOR, M. & ADAMS, R. D. (1957). *Brain*, **80**, 319.
BARBEAU, A. (1965). *Proc. 8th Int. Congr. Neurol.* p. 257.
BARBEAU, A. (1966). In *Symposium über progressive Muskeldystrophie*, ed), Kuhn, E. Berlin: Springer-Verlag.
BARNES, S. (1932). *Brain*, **55**, 1.
BARWICK, D. D. (1963). In *Research in Muscular Dystrophy*, p. 23. Pitman: London.
BARWICK, D. D., OSSELTON, J. W., & WALTON, J. N. (1965). *J. Neurol. Psycihat.* **28** 103.
BATTEN, F. E. (1903). *Q. J. Med.* **3**, 313.
BATTEN, F. E. & GIBB, H. P. (1909). *Brain*, **32**, 187.
BECKER, P. E. (1953). *Dystrophia Musculorum Progressiva*. Stuttgart: Thieme.
BECKER, P. E. (1957). *Acta genet. statist. med.*, **7**, 303.
BETHLEM, J. & MEYJES, F. E. P. (1960). *Folia psychiat. neurol. neurochir. neerl.* **63**, 246.
BIEMOND, A. (1955). *Acta psychiat. neurol. scand.* **30**, 25.
BIEMOND, A. (1966). In *Symposium über progressive Muskeldystrophie*, ed. Kuh, E. Berlin: Springer-Verlag.
BLYTH, H. & PUGH, R. J. (1959). *Ann. hum. Genet.* **23**, 127.
BRAY, G. M., KAARSOO, M. & ROSS, R. T. (1965). *Neurology, Minneap.*, **15**, 678.
BROWN, G. L. & HARVEY, A. M. (1939). *Brain*, **62**, 341.
BUCHTHAL, F. (1962). *Wld Neurol.* **3**, 16.
BUCHTHAL, F. & PINELLI, P. (1953). *Neurology, Minneap.* **3**, 424.
BUCHTHAL, F., ROSENFALCK, P., & ERMINIO, F. (1960). *Neurology, Minneap.* **10** 398.
CARUSO, G. & BUCHTHAL, F. (1965). *Brain*, **88**, 29.
CAUGHEY, J. E. (1952). *J. Bone Jt. Surg.* **34B**, 343.
CAUGHEY, J. E. & MYRIANTHOPOULOS, N. C. (1963). *Dystrophia Myotonica and Related Disorders*. Springfield, Illinois: Thomas.
CHUNG, C. S. & MORTON, N. E. (1959). *Am. J. hum. Genet.* **11**, 339.
CHUNG, C. S., MORTON, N. E., & PETERS, H. A. (1960). *Am. J. hum. Genet.* **12**, 52.
CONNEN, P. E., MURPHY, E. G., & DONOHUE, W. L. (1963). *Can. med. Ass. J.* **89**, 983.

COOMES, E. N. (1965). *Ann. rheum. Dis.* **24**, 465.
DAVEY, M. R. & WOOLF, A. L. (1965). *Proc. 6th Int. Congr. EEG Clin. Neurophysiol.* p. 653.
DE LANGE, C. (1937). *Acta paediat. Stockh.* **20**, Suppl. III.
DODGE, P. R., GAMSTORP, I., BYERS, R. K., & RUSSELL, P. (1965). *Pediatrics, Springfield,* **35**, 3.
DREYFUS, J. C. & SCHAPIRA, G. (1962). *Klin. Wschr.* **40**, 373.
DUBOWITZ, V. (1960). *Brain,* **83**, 432.
DUBOWITZ, V. (1963). *J. Neurol. Neurosurg. Psychiat.* **26**, 322.
DUBOWITZ, V. & PEARSE, A. G. E. (1960). *Lancet,* **2**, 23.
DUCHENNE, G. B. (1868). *Archs gen. Med.* **11**, 5, 179, 305, 420, 552.
EMERY, A. E. H. (1963). *Lancet,* **1**, 1126.
EMERY, A. E. H. (1965a). *J. Génét. hum.* **14**, 318.
EMERY, A. E. H. (1956b). *J. med. Génét.* **2**, 1.
EMERY, A. E. H. (1965c). In *Research in Muscular Dystrophy,* 3rd series, p. 90. London: Pitman.
EMERY, A. E. H. (1966). *J. med. Genet.* **3**, 92.
ENGEL, W. K., FOSTER, J. B., HUGHES, B. P., HUXLEY, H. E., & MAHLER, R. (1961). *Brain,* **84**, 167.
ENGEL, W. K., WANKO, T., & FENICHEL, G. M. (1964). *Archs Neurol., Chicago,* **11**, 22.
ERB, W. H. (1884). *Dts. Arch. klin. Med.,* **34**, 467.
ERDBRINK, W. L. (1957). *Archs Ophthal. N.Y.* **57**, 335.
EULENBURG, A. (1886). *Neurol. Zentbl.* **5**, 265.
FARMER, T. W., BUCHTHAL, F., & ROSENFALCK, P. (1959). *Neurology, Minneap.* **9**, 747.
FERRIER, R., BAMATTER, F., & KLEIN, D. (1965). *J. med. Genet.* **2**, 38.
FORD, F. R. (1960). *Diseases of the Nervous System in Infancy, Childhood and Adolescence,* 4th ed. Springfield, Illinois: Thomas.
FRIEDREICH, N. (1863). *Virchows Arch. path. Anat. Physiol.,* **28**, 474.
FUCHS, E. (1890). *Archs Ophthal. N.Y.* **36**, 234.
FUKUYAMA, Y., YAMADA, M., & KAWAZURA, M. (1961). *Brain Nerve, Tokyo,* **13**, 261.
GAMSTORP, I. (1956). *Acta paediat. Stockh.,* Suppl. 108.
GARDNER-MEDWIN, D. (1968). *J. Neurol. Neurosurg. Psychiat.,* **31**, 124.
GARDNER-MEDWIN, D., HUDGSON, P., & WALTON, J. N. (1967). *J. Neurol. Sci.,* **5**, 121.
GILLAM, P. M. S., HEAF, P. J. D., KAUFMAN, L., & LUCAS, B. G. B. (1964). *Thorax,* **19**, 112.
GOWERS, W. R. (1879). *Pseudo-hypertrophic Muscular Paralysis.* Churchill: London.
GOWERS, W. R. (1902). *Br. med. J.* **2**, 89.
GUBBAY, S. S., WALTON, J. N., & PEARCE, G. W. (1966). *J. Neurol. Neurosurg. Psychiat.* **29**, 500.
HAUSMANOWA-PETRUSEWICZ, I., PROT, J., NIEBROJ-DOBOSZ, I., EMERYK, B., WASOWICZ, B., SLUCKA, C., HETNARSKA, L., BANDARZEWSKA, B., & PUCEK, Z. (1965). *Proc. 8th Int. Congr. Neurol.* p. 635.
HAVARD, C. W. H., CAMPBELL, E. D. R., ROSS, H. B., & SPENCE, A. W. (1963). *C. J. Med.* **32**, 145.
HUDGSON, P., GARDNER-MEDWIN, D., FULTHORPE, J. J., & WALTON, J. N. (1967). *Neurology Minneap.* **17**, 1125.
HUDGSON, P., GARDNER-MEDWIN, D., PENNINGTON, R. J. T., & WALTON, J. N. (1967). *J. Neurol. Neurosurg. Psychiat.,* **30**, 416.
HUDGSON, P., WALTON, J. N., & PEARCE, G. W. (1967). *Brain,* **90**, 565.
HUGHES, B. P. (1962). *Br. med. J.,* **2**, 953.
HUTCHINSON, J. (1879). *Med.-chir. Trans.* **62**, 307.
JEQUIER, M. (1950). *Schweiz. med. Wschr.* **80**, 593.
KILOH, L. G. & NEVIN, S. (1951). *Brain* **74**, 115.
KLOEPFER, H. W. & TALLEY, C. (1958). *Ann. hum. Genet.* **22**, 138.
KRABBE, K. H. (1958). *Acta psychiat. neurol. scand.* **33**, 94.

KUGELBERG, E. (1949). *J. Neurol. Neurosurg. Psychiat.* **12**, 129.
KUGELBERG, E. & WELANDER, L. (1956). *A.M.A. Arch. Neurol. Psychiat.* **75**, 500.
LAMY, M. & DE GROUCHY, J. (1954). *J. Génét. hum.* **3**, 219.
LANDOUZY, L. & DEJERINE, J. (1884). *C.r.hebd. Séanc. Acad. Sci. Paris,* **98**, 53.
LEYBURN, P., THOMSON, W. H. S., & WALTON, J. N. (1961). *Ann. hum. Genet.* **25**, 41.
LEYDEN, E. (1876). *Klinik der Rückenmarks-Krankheiten,* Vol. 2, p. 531. Berlin: Hirschwald.
MAAS, O. & PATERSON, A. S. (1939). *Brain* **62**, 198.
MAAS, O. & PATERSON, A. S. (1950). *Brain* **73**, 318.
MARSHALL, J. (1959). *Brain* **82**, 221.
MILHORAT, A. T. & WOLFF, H. G. (1943). *Archs Neurol. Psychiat., Chicago* **49**, 641.
MÖBIUS, P. J. (1879). *Samml. klin. Vortr.* **171**, 1505.
MORTON, N. E. & CHUNG, C. S. (1959). *Amer. J. hum. Genet.* **11**, 360.
MÜLLER, R. & KUGELBERG, E. (1959). *J. Neurol. Neurosurg. Psychiat.* **2**, 314.
NEVIN, S. (1936). *Q. Jl Med.* **5**, 51.
NISSEN, K. (1923). *Z. klin. Med.* **97**, 58.
OPPENHEIM, H. (1900). *Mschr. Psychiat. Neurol.* **8**, 233.
PAINE, R. S. (1963). *Devl. Med. Child Neurol.* **5**, 115.
PEARCE, G. W. & WALTON, J. N. (1962). *J. Path. Bact.* **83**, 535.
PEARCE, J. M. S., PENNINGTON, R. J. T., & WALTON, J. N. (1964). *J. Neurol. Neurosurg. Psychiat.* **27**, 181.
PEARSON, C. M. (1962). *Brain* **85**, 109.
PENROSE, L. S. (1947). *Ann. Eugen.* **14**, 125.
PHILIP, U., WALTON, J. N., & SMITH, C. A. B. (1956). *Ann. hum. Genet.* **21**, 155.
PRICE, H. M., GORDON, G. B., PEARSON, C. M., MUNSAT, T. L., & BLUMBERG, J. M. (1965). *Proc. nat. Acad. Sci. U.S.A.* **54**, 1398.
PRUZANSKI, W. (1966). *Brain* **89**, 563.
RAMSAY, I. D. (1965). *Q. Jl Med.* **34**, 255.
REFSUM, S., LOUNUM, A., SJAASTAD, O., & ENGESET, A. (1967). *Neurology, Minneap.* **17**, 345.
RICHTERICH, R., ROSIN, S., AEBI, U., & ROSSI, E. (1963). *Am. J. hum. Genet.* **15**, 133.
ROSMAN, N. P. & KAKULAS, B. A. (1966). *Brain* **89**, 769.
ROWLAND, L. P. & ESKENAZI, A. N. (1956). *Neurology, Minneap.* **6**, 667.
SANDERSON, K. V. & ADEY, W. R. (1952). *J. Neurol. Neurosurg. Psychiat.* **15**, 200.
SCHAPIRA, F., DREYFUS, J. C., SCHAPIRA, G., & DEMOS, J. (1960). *Revue fr. Étud. clin. biol.* **5**, 990.
SHORT, J. K. (1963). *Neurology Minneap.* **13**, 526.
SHY, G. M., ENGEL, W. K., SOMERS, J. E., & WANKO, T. (1963). *Brain* **86**, 793.
SHY, G. M. & GONATAS, N. K. (1964). *Science, N.Y.* **145**, 493.
SHY, G. M., GONATAS, N. K., & PEREZ, M. C. (1966). *Brain* **89**, 133.
SHY, G. M. & MAGEE, K. R. (1956). *Brain* **79**, 610.
SILVESTRI, T. (1909). *Gazz. Osp. Clin.* **30**, 577.
SPILLER, W. G. (1907). *J. nerv. ment. Dis.* **34**, 14.
SPILLER, W. G. (1913). *Brain* **36**, 75.
SPIRO, A. J., SHY, G. M. & GONATAS, N. K. (1966). *Arch. Neurol. Chicago* **14**, 1.
STEINERT, H. (1909). *Dt. Z. NervHeilk.* **37**, 58.
STEPHENS, J. & LEWIN, E. (1965). *J. Neurol. Neurosurg. Psychiat.* **28**, 104.
STEVENSON, A. C. (1953). *Ann. Eugen.* **18**, 50.
THOMASEN, E. (1948). *Myotonia—Thomsen's Disease (Myotonia congenita), Paramyotonia, Dystrophia Myotonica.* Universitetsforlaget, Aarhus.
THOMSEN, J. (1876). *Arch. Psychiat. NervenKrankh.* **6**, 706.
TURNER, J. W. A. (1940). *Brain* **63**, 163.
TURNER, J. W. A. (1949). *Brain* **72**, 25.
TURNER, J. W. A. & LEES, F. (1962). *Brain* **85**, 733.
TYLER, F. H. & WINTROBE, M. M. (1950). *Ann. intern. Med.* **32**, 72.
VAN DEN BOSCH, J. (1963). In *Research in Muscular Dystrophy,* p. 23. London: Pitman.

VANIER, T. M. (1960). *Br. med. J.* **2**, 1284.

VICTOR, M., HAYES, R. & ADAMS, R. D. (1962). *New Engl. J. Med.* **267**, 1267.

WALSH, F. B. (1957). *Clinical Neuro-ophthalmology*, 2nd ed. London: Bailliere, Tindall & Cox.

WALTON, J. N. (1952). *J. Neurol. Neurosurg. Psychiat.*, **15**, 219.

WALTON, J. N. (1955). *Ann. hum. Genet.*, **20**, 1.

WALTON, J. N. (1956a). *Ann. hum. Genet.*, **21**, 40.

WALTON, J. N. (1956b). *Lancet*, **1**, 1023.

WALTON, J. N. (1957). *J. Neurol. Neurosurg. Psychiat.*, **20**, 144.

WALTON, J. N. (1960). *Res. Publs Ass. nerv. ment. Dis.* **38**, 378.

WALTON, J. N. (1963). *Muscular Dystrophy in Man and Animals*, Chap. 7, ed. Bourne, G. H. and Golarz, M. N. Basel: Karger.

WALTON, J. N. (1964a). *Br. med. J.*, **1**, 1271, 1344.

WALTON, J. N. (1964b). *Disorders of Voluntary Muscle*, Chap. 11, ed. Walton, J. N. London: Churchill.

WALTON, J. N. (1965a). *Biochemical Aspects of Neurological Disorders*, Chap. 1, ed. Cumings, J. N. and Kremer, M., Oxford: Blackwell.

WALTON, J. N. (1965b). In *Muscle*, ed. Paul, W. M., Daniel, E. E., Kay, C. M. and Monckton, G., Oxford: Pergamon Press.

WALTON, J. N. (1966). *Abstr. Wld Med.* **40**, 1, 81.

WALTON, J. N. & ADAMS, R. D. (1953). *Polymyositis*. Edinburgh: Livingstone.

WALTON, J. N., GESCHWIND, N., & SIMPSON, J. A. (1956). *J. Neurol. Neurosurg. Psychiat.* **19**, 224.

WALTON, J. N. & NATTRASS, F. J. (1954). *Brain* **77**, 169.

WALTON, J. N. & WARRICK, C. K. (1954). *Br. J. Radiol.* **27**, 1.

WELANDER, L. (1951). *Acta med. scand.*, Suppl. 265, 1.

WELANDER, L. (1957). *Acta genet. statist. med.* **7**, 321.

WELANDER, L. (1966). In *Symposium über progressive Muskeldystrophie*, ed. Kuhn, E. Berlin: Springer-Verlag.

WILLIAMS, R. S. (1959). *Lancet*, **1**, 698.

WILLISON, R. G. (1965). *Proc. 6th Int. Congr. EEG Clin. Neurophysiol.*, p. 711.

WILSON, K. M., EVANS, K. A., & CARTER, C. O. (1965). *Br. med. J.* **1**, 750.

WOCHNER, R. D., DREWS, G., STROBER, W., & WALDMANN, T. A. (1966). *J. clin. Invest.*, **45**, 321.

BIOCHEMICAL ABNORMALITIES IN MUSCULAR DYSTROPHY

R. J. PENNINGTON

EACH of the inherited diseases classified as a muscular dystrophy presumably results from a failure or defect in the biosynthesis of a specific protein, due to an abnormal base sequence in the chromosomal DNA. Such a protein, which must evidently be essential to the maintenance of the muscle fibres is, on grounds of probability, most likely to be an enzyme. It can be assumed that a different protein is involved in each type of human muscular dystrophy, since each has a different pattern of transmission.

Up to the present time, however, a noteworthy feature of the changes observed in dystrophic muscle has been their lack of specificity. Comparison of the biochemical and histological studies on the human muscular dystrophies, inherited animal myopathies (mouse, hamster, chicken, duck), vitamin E deficiency myopathy and neurogenic atrophy shows little evidence of alterations limited to a particular disease. Many of the changes, in fact, appear to be common to most or all types of muscle degeneration. Such a stereotyped sequence of secondary changes in muscle following various primary defects renders the identification of the latter much more difficult.

Location of Primary Abnormality

The classification of the human muscular dystrophies as primary diseases of muscle implies that the genetic abnormality is manifested directly in the muscle fibres. It is recognized, however, that this is based largely upon negative evidence, i.e., the absence of associated disease in other organs, particularly in the nervous system, damage to which, as is well known, can lead to muscle weakness and atrophy. A firm answer to this problem would evidently be of immense value to further research by making possible an appropriate concentration of effort. In principle it would seem that tissue cultures studies may be able to throw a clearer light on this question. A difference in growth characteristics between cultured cells from dystrophic and normal muscle, thus isolated from the rest of the body, would lend support to the assumption of a primary muscle disease. It is difficult to obtain satisfactory cultures from mature muscle but Geiger & Garvin (1957) nevertheless reported differences between normal and dystrophic muscle in culture. Dystrophic cells had a shorter dormancy period, were more granular and developed no cross-striations. After about one month they underwent marked hypertrophy, then broke up and degenerated. Normal cells, on the other hand, were satisfactorily subcultured for a year.

23

One would like to see this work confirmed and extended quantitatively. Studies with muscle from affected foetuses, if ever available, or with mature muscle damaged to promote regeneration might be more valuable.

In the case of hereditary myopathy in the mouse, numerous tissue culture studies (Pearce, 1963; O'Steen, 1963; Ross, 1965) have indicated abnormalities in myoblasts from dystrophic muscle. The primary nature of the disease has been confirmed by homotransplantation (Laird & Timmer, 1965) and parabiosis (Pope, Murphy & West, 1964) experiments.

Golarz, Bourne & Richardson (1961), on the basis of histochemical evidence for increased endomysial phosphatase activities in human dystrophic muscle proposed that the primary abnormality was in connective tissue. However, it seems likely that these changes result simply from the proliferation of endomysial connective tissue, which is generally accepted as a secondary phenomenon.

The exclusion of the nervous system as the origin of the muscular dystrophies has found support in the pattern of histopathological changes, as opposed to the simple atrophy of fibres which predominates in neurogenic muscle disease, and also in the relatively late manifestation of muscle weakness in muscular dystrophy, which is not markedly evident until a large proportion of the fibres are degenerating. However, recent work on nerve-muscle interrelationships suggests that the nervous system may exert a more discriminating control over the metabolism of muscle fibres than was realized. Romanul & Van der Meulen (1966) and Dubowitz & Newman (1967) have shown by cross-innervation that the characteristic enzyme profile of red and white fibres is determined by their motor nerves. McPherson & Tokunaga (1966) found that cross-innervation altered the relative amounts of myoglobin in the two types. Dr. Dubowitz will undoubtedly discuss this work later in this Symposium. Furthermore a recent report (Korr, Wilkinson & Chornock, 1967) provides evidence for the passage of "trophic" factors from nerve to muscle, a possibility which has often been suggested. These workers succeeded in labelling hypoglossal nuclei in the brain with ^{32}P-phosphate and ^{14}C-amino acids and demonstrating the passage of radioactive isotope along the nerve and into the muscle fibres of the tongue. Evidently, the existence of a more subtle control of muscle metabolism by the nerve, involving perhaps control over the synthesis of specific muscle proteins, suggested by these studies, would allow for the possibility of muscle damage resulting from changes in the nerve without the gross interference with the passage of impulses, which occurs in the recognized neurogenic muscle diseases. One is therefore less confident in excluding the nervous system as the original site of expression of the gene defect in the muscular dystrophies.

Decreased Enzyme Activity of Dystrophic Muscle

I will now consider some of the chemical changes which have been

described in human dystrophic muscle and discuss their possible significance. A lot of work has been concerned with measurement of muscle
enzyme activities in dystrophy; in fact most of the more abundant muscle
enzymes have now been studied in this respect. Several display a decreased
activity and Table 1 summarizes results from a number of sources. In order
to make comparison of enzyme activities in dystrophic and normal muscle
as meaningful as possible it is necessary to allow for the considerable
increase in collagen and often of fat in dystrophic muscle, so that results
may be related as far as possible to metabolically active tissue. Table I is

Table I. *Decreased enzyme activities in human dystrophic muscle.*

Adenylate kinase	Lactate dehydrogenase
Aldolase	Malate dehydrogenase
AMP deaminase	Phosphoglucomutase
Aspartate aminotransferase	Phosphoglycerate kinase
Creatine kinase	Phosphorylase
Enolase	Pyruvate kinase
Glyceraldehyde phosphate	
dehydrogenase	Triosephosphate isomerase
αGlycerophosphate	
dehydrogenase	

Based on data from: Dreyfus, Schapira, Schapira & Demos
(1956); Heyck, Laudahn & Lüders (1963); Pennington (1962).

based upon activities expressed per unit of 'non-collagen nitrogen', or
'extractable protein'.

The enzymes showing reduced activity are largely those which are
present in the sarcoplasm and include most of the enzymes involved in
glycolysis. They normally constitute probably about three-quarters of the
total sarcoplasmic protein. The magnitude of the decline of different
enzymes varies considerably—thus aldolase shows a particularly large
fall and aminotransferase only a slight one—and generally progresses with
the disease; in fact in the case of one or two of the enzymes of Table 1
increased activities compared with normal muscle have been reported in
the early stages. As would be expected from the decline in individual
enzymes, the overall rate of glycolysis is low—it may be as little as one-fifth
of the normal. Such changes are not an inevitable consequence of muscle
atrophy, since aldolase and overall glycolysis rate do not decline in myopathic mouse muscle (Mayers & Epstein, 1962; Srivastava & Berlinguet,
1964). However, similar changes in some of the enzymes have been reported
in denervated muscle and neurogenic muscle disease (Hogan, Dawson &
Romanul, 1965; Vignos & Lefkowitz, 1959). It can be assumed, therefore,
that these decreased enzyme activities are secondary changes, particularly

as they are less evident in the early stages. It has been suggested that the altered activities result from leakage of enzymes from the diseased fibres, a well-known phenomenon in muscular dystrophy. This seems an inadequate explanation, however, for a number of reasons. Thus, some enzymes, particularly AMP deaminase, which decline in muscle, show little corresponding rise in the blood (Table II). Also, there is normally little or no

TABLE II. *Serum enzymes in Duchenne-type muscular dystrophy.*
The figures represent approximately the maximum values (i.u./l. of
serum at 37° C.) recorded for normals and patients.

	Normal	Duchenne
Creatine kinase	60	23,000
Phosphoglucomutase	3	110
Aldolase	7	160
Lactate dehydrogenase	700	4,400
Aspartate aminotransferase	50	250
Alanine ,,	40	200
Glucosephosphate isomerase	220	800
Triosephosphate ,,	700	2,400
Malate dehydrogenase	170	520
AMP deaminase	6	10
Adenylate kinase	60	90

Data quoted from Pennington (1965).

increase in blood enzymes in neurogenic muscle atrophy. Moreover it appears that, even in Duchenne dystrophy, the rate of loss by leakage is extremely slow compared with the rate of physiological turnover of muscle proteins; thus isotope studies (Schapira, Kruh, Dreyfus & Schapira, 1960) suggest a half-life of about 20 days for muscle aldolase. It would require only a very slight adjustment in the synthesis-breakdown balance to compensate for the loss of enzyme due to leakage.

It would appear, therefore, that there is a decreased rate of synthesis (or increased breakdown) of these enzymes in dystrophic muscle. This will be discussed later but I should like to mention here that many of the enzymes concerned manifest in normal animals and humans a marked increase in activity during development (Kendrick-Jones & Perry, 1967a; Hooft, de Laey & Lambert, 1966; Dawson & Kaplan, 1965). Hence the levels of these enzymes in dystrophic muscle tends to resemble that of normal muscle at an earlier stage of development.

Isoenzyme Changes

Other investigations have been concerned with patterns of isoenzymes in dystrophic muscle. Isoenzymes are different proteins (or contain varying proportions of the same protein sub-units) with similar enzyme activity.

They are usually separated and identified by zone electrophoresis. Isoenzymes of lactate dehydrogenase have been studied the most thoroughly; five are recognized and in most mature muscles the predominating one is LDH 5, which moves the slowest on electrophoresis. It was shown first by Wieme & Lauryssens (1962) and confirmed by many others that in human dystrophic muscle there is a reduction, sometimes very marked, in the relative amount of the LDH 5 component. A similar change is however seen often in other types of muscle disease including neurogenic atrophy (e.g. Brody, 1964). Dreyfus, Demos, Schapira & Schapira (1962) pointed out that the abnormal LDH pattern in dystrophic muscle resembles the pattern seen in normal foetal muscle. It appears therefore that the changes in LDH 5 are similar to the changes in the enzymes mentioned above and are probably due to a similar cause. These isoenzyme changes have been observed at a very early stage in the development of human muscular dystrophy and perhaps the normal mature pattern is never attained. This, in fact, is the case in the dystrophic chicken, where the level of LDH 5 does not show the steep rise during the weeks following hatching which is seen in the normal (Dawson & Kaplan, 1965). A decreased LDH 5 has also been found in muscle of some female carriers of Duchenne dystrophy (Emery, 1965).

Recent studies on other isoenzymes, although less well substantiated, have indicated similar results. Malate dehydrogenase (Cao et al., 1966) in mature human muscle shows two isoenzymes, derived respectively from the sarcoplasm and mitochondria. The latter isoenzyme was almost absent from foetal muscle and in 2 out of 6 cases of Duchenne muscular dystrophy. Schapira (1966) and Schapira, Dreyfus & Schapira (1966) respectively found that the isoenzymes of creatine kinase and aldolase in rabbit muscle tended towards the foetal pattern in denervation atrophy.

Other Muscle Proteins

Yet another example of a foetal protein pattern in dystrophic muscle is provided by studies on myoglobin. This haem protein, the oxygen carrier in muscle fibres, is present to the extent of 2-3 mg. per g. of fresh human muscle and some workers, impressed by the existence of several abnormal haemoglobins, had suggested that muscular dystrophy may be a 'myoglobinopathy'. The most careful and extensive studies have been carried out by Perkoff (1964, 1966). He separated myoglobin from adult human muscle on DEAE-cellulose and found a major component ('myoglobin A') and a smaller peak ('F3'). Foetal muscle (up to 13 days post partum), in contrast, contained very little myoglobin A and the predominant fraction was F3. The component myoglobins could be distinguished also by starch-gel electrophoresis. In two cases of childhood muscular dystrophy examined myoglobin A was greatly diminished and a similar picture was found in a case of dermatomyositis and one of myoglobinuria. However the pattern was normal in cases of myotonic and facioscapulohumeral dystrophy. Whorton, Hudgins & Conners (1961) had previously reported myoglobin spectrum changes in the direction of the foetal pattern in muscular dystrophy. The failure of some workers to confirm the existence of a foetal myoglobin was perhaps explained by Perkoff's evidence that its molecular size may be similar to that of haemoglobin and it would therefore probably be removed by the procedures used to remove the latter.

The most abundant protein in muscle is, of course, myosin. A number of workers (e.g. Trayer & Perry, 1966) have reported that the specific ATPase activity of myosin is low in foetal muscle. It would evidently be of considerable interest to know whether myosin in dystrophic muscle falls into line and has a correspondingly low ATPase activity.

Cause of Enzyme Changes

Until much more work has been done it will not be possible to say whether the diminished concentrations of these various proteins in dystrophic muscle and the corresponding resemblances to foetal muscle are due to the same cause. One possibility is that they represent responses to the diminished muscular activity in the disease. It has been demonstrated (Kendrick-Jones & Perry, 1967a) that the previously mentioned increase in creatine kinase and other enzymes in rabbit muscle during development can be correlated with the use of the muscles. These workers have also shown (Kendrick-Jones & Perry, 1965) that exercise or electrical stimulation of muscle produces a rapid increase in muscle creatine kinase. This is prevented by puromycin, an inhibitor of protein synthesis, and hence is probably due to synthesis of more enzyme (Kendrick-Jones & Perry, 1967b). Dawson & Kaplan (1965) found that in chickens the LDH isoenzyme pattern reached its adult form in leg muscle much earlier than in breast muscle, again parallelling the activity of the muscles. Since the contraction of phasic muscles depends on the energy of glycolysis it is perhaps not surprising that the amounts of the glycolytic enzymes should be adjusted to match activity. A similar argument applies to creatine kinase and probably AMP deaminase, adenylate kinase and LDH 5; the latter is thought to be the LDH isoenzyme most important in anaerobic glycolysis.

It is, of course, of interest to inquire how such adaptive changes may occur. They could, for example, be directly connected with the fact that fewer nerve impulses reach the muscle. If so, a possible mechanism is that the nerve impulses in some way facilitate the transfer of 'trophic' substances from nerve to muscle. Such compounds may perhaps function by stimulating the synthesis of specific enzymes and other proteins in muscle in the way that many hormones are thought to act on their target tissues, possibly by combining with repressor molecules which inhibit gene activity. On the other hand it is conceivable that the muscle exerts its own control over the synthesis of these enzymes. It is possible, for instance, that some product of muscle glycolysis stimulates the synthesis of glycolytic enzymes, the level of which would then be automatically related to muscle activity.

It may be, however, that the enzyme decreases in dystrophic muscle are not simply the consequence of diminished muscular activity, in which case one must speculate differently. Perhaps owing to chemical and metabolic changes within the muscle these suggested regulating factors from the nerve are unable to reach their site of action or are rapidly destroyed. Finally, one cannot exclude the possibility that the primary change is in the nerve, causing interference in the supply of regulators to the muscle. This mechanism, unlike the previous possibilities, would imply that the one or other of the protein changes mentioned could represent the initial change in the muscle.

The following enzymes have been reported to remain unchanged in activity in dystrophic muscles; succinate dehydrogenase, cytochrome oxidase, fumarase, aconitase. All these are involved in the oxidation of carbohydrate and fat and are therefore probably more important with regard to maintenance or steady contraction. Perhaps if measured in predominantly red muscles they would be seen to decline in dystrophy.

Increased Enzyme Activities

I will now consider the enzymes, of which there are a considerable number (Table III), which display an increased activity in dystrophic muscle.

Table III. *Increased enzyme activities in human dystrophic muscle.*

Glucose 6-phosphate dehydrogenase Phosphogluconate dehydrogenase Glutamate dehydrogenase	Cathepsins Ribonucleases (acid and alkaline) Aryl sulphatase 5'-Nucleotidase

Based on data from: Heyck, Laudahn & Lüders (1963); Pennington (1962); Hooft, de Laey & Lambert (1966; Abdullah, Pennington & Robinson (unpublished).

There can be a several-fold increase in the activity of the NADP-linked enzymes glucose 6-phosphate dehydrogenase and phosphogluconate dehydrogenase. It is not known whether other enzymes of the pentose phosphate pathway show a similar increase. The increased activity of these two enzymes seems to be a very common response to muscle damage, having been observed in mouse myopathy, denervated muscle and in myopathies due to drugs and to viral infection. It is probably due to the proliferation of connective tissue, which contains relatively large amounts of these enzymes (Woessner & Boucek, 1959), whilst muscle contains very little. In fact Garcia-Bunuel & Garcia-Bunuel (1967) found a parallel between the activity of these enzymes in denervated muscle and the collagen content and suggest that they are confined to the connective tissue. Smith (1965) however, in histochemical studies, claimed to find glucose 6-phosphate dehydrogenase in regenerating muscle fibres although not in normal mature ones.

The increased activity of the hydrolytic enzymes is seen also in muscle atrophy due to other causes, although it appears to be generally smaller in denervation atrophy, in which activity may even be decreased in the later stages (Weinstock & Lukacs, 1965). It has been attributed to the presence of invading macrophages, since macrophages are known to be rich in these hydrolases (Cohn & Weiner, 1964). However what evidence there is does not support this suggestion. Weinstock, Marshall & Jenkins (1962) reported that the electrophoretic behaviour of cathepsin from muscle of rabbits with nutritional muscular dystrophy was different from that obtained from peritoneal macrophages. Iodice, Leong & Weinstock (1966) reported identical chromatographic behaviour of cathepsin A from normal and dystrophic mouse muscle. Assuming then that there is an increase in the true muscle hydrolases it might be supposed that this results from an increase in the number of lysosomes in the fibres, since these organelles are the site of such enzymes in some tissues. The existence of lysosomes in muscle fibres is still disputed however. Furthermore, we have found an increase in neutral and alkaline proteinase and ribonuclease in dystrophic muscle and such alkaline hydrolases have not been shown to be associated with lysosomes in any tissue. In fact, in homogenates of brain, Marks & Lajtha (1963) obtained evidence for a different distribution of acid and neutral proteinase among the various particle fractions. Future work will show whether the increase in both acid and alkaline hydrolases in dystrophic muscle is due to a common cause.

REFERENCES

BRODY, I. A. (1964). *Neurology, Minneap.* **14**, 1091.
CAO, A., MACCIOTTA, A., FIORELLI, G., MANNUCCI, P. M., & IDEO, G. (1966). *Enzym. biol. clin.* **7**, 156.
DAWSON, D. M. & KAPLAN, N. O. (1965). *J. biol. chem.* **240**, 3215.
COHN, Z. A. & WIENER, E. (1964). *J. exp. Med.* **118**, 991.
DREYFUS, J. C., SCHAPIRA, G., SCHAPIRA, F., & DEMOS, J. (1956). *Clinica Chim. Acta* **1**, 434.
DREYFUS, J C., DEMOS, J., SCHAPIRA, F., & SCHAPIRA, G. (1962). *C. r. hebd. Séanc. Acad. Sci. Paris* **254**, 4384.
DUBOWITZ, V. & NEWMAN, D. L. (1967). *Nature, Lond.* **214**, 840.
EMERY, A. E. H. (1965). In *Research in Muscular Dystrophy*, p. 90. London: Pitman.
GARCIA-BUNUEL, L. & GARCIA-BUNUEL, V. M. (1967). *Nature, Lond.* **213**, 913.
GEIGER, R. S. & GARVIN, J. S. (1957). *J. Neuropath. exp. Neurol.* **16**, 532.
GOLARZ, N., BOURNE, G. H., & RICHARDSON, H. D. (1961). *J. Histochem. Cytochem.* **9**, 132.
HEYCK, H., LAUDAHN, G., & LUDERS, C. J. (1963). *Klin. Wschr.* **41**, 500.
HOGAN, E. L., DAWSON, D. M., & ROMANUL, F. C. A. (1965). *Archs Neurol., Chicago* **13**, 274.
HOOFT, C. DE LAEY, P. & LAMBERT, Y. (1966). *Revue fr. Etud. clin. biol.* **11**, 510.
IODICE, A. A., LEONG, V., & WEINSTOCK, I. M. (1966). *Archs Biochem. Biophys.* **117**, 477.
KENDRICK-JONES, J. & PERRY, S. V. (1965). *Nature, Lond.* **208**, 1068.
KENDRICK-JONES, J. & PERRY, S. V. (1967a). *Biochem. J.* **103**, 207.
KENDRICK-JONES, J. & PERRY, S. V. (1967b). *Nature, Lond.* **213**, 406.
KORR, I. M., WILKINSON, P. N., & CHORNOCK, F. W. (1967). *Science, N.Y.* **155**, 342.
LAIRD, J. L. & TIMMER, R. F. (1965). *Archs Path.* **80**, 442.
MCPHERSON, A. & TOKUNAGA, J. (1966). *J. Physiol., Lond.* **188**, 121.
MARKS, N. & LAJTHA, A. (1963). *Biochem. J.* **89**, 438.
MAYERS, G. L. & EPSTEIN, N. (1962). *Proc. Soc. exp. Biol.* **111**, 450.
O'STEEN, W. K. (1963). *Texas Rep. Biol. Med.* **21**, 369.
PEARCE, G. W. (1963). In *Research in Muscular Dystrophy*, p. 75. London: Pitman.
PENNINGTON, R. J. (1965). In *Biochemical Aspects of Neurological Disorders* ed. Cummings, J. N. and Kremer M., p. 28. Oxford: Blackwell.
PENNINGTON, R. J. (1962). *Proc. Ass. clin. Biochem.* **2**, 17.
PERKOFF, G. T. (1964). *New Engl. J. Med.* **270**, 263.
PERKOFF, G. T. (1966). *J. Lab. clin. Med.* **67**, 585.
POPE, R. S., MURPHY, E. D., & WEST, W. T. (1964). *Am. J. Physiol.* **207**, 449.
ROMANUL, F. C. A. & VAN DER MEULEN, J. P. (1965). *Nature, Lond.* **212**, 1369.
ROSS, K. F. A. (1965). In *Research in Muscular Dystrophy*, p. 119. London: Pitman.
SCHAPIRA, F. (1966). *C. r. hebd. Séanc. Acad. Sci. Paris* (D) **262**, 2291.
SCHAPIRA, F., DREYFUS, J. C., & SCHAPIRA, G. (1966). *Enzym. biol. clin.* **7**, 98.
SCHAPIRA, G., KRUH, J., DREYFUS, J. C., & SCHAPIRA, F. (1960. *J. biol. Chem.* **235**, 1738.
SMITH, B. (1965). In *Research in Muscular Dystrophy*, p. 132. London: Pitman.
SRIVASTAVA, U. & BERLINGUET, L. (1964). *Can. J. Biochem. Physiol.* **42**, 1301.
TRAYER, I. P. & PERRY, S. V. (1966). *Biochem. Z.* **345**, 87.
VIGNOS, P. J. & LEFKOWITZ, M. (1959). *J. clin Invest.* **38**, 873.
WEINSTOCK, I. M., MARSHALL, M., & JENKINS, H. (1962). *Fedn Proc. Fedn Am. Socs exp. Biol.* **21**, 320.
WEINSTOCK, I. M. & LUKACS, M. (1965). *Enzym. Biol. Clin.* **5**, 89.
WHORTON, C. M., HUDGINS, P. C., & CONNORS, J. J. (1961). *New Engl. J. Med.* **265**, 1242.
WIEME, R. J. & LAURYSSENS, M. J. (1962). *Lancet* **1**, 433.
WOESSNER, J. F., jr. & BOUCEK, R. J. (1959). *J. biol. Chem.* **234**, 3296.

CHEMICAL AND STRUCTURAL CHANGES IN MUSCLE: THE IMPORTANCE OF THE NERVOUS SYSTEM

Victor Dubowitz

The title of this paper may appear out of context in a symposium on inherited disorders of brain and muscle but since the purpose of a symposium is to provoke thought and discussion, I intend to develop the thesis that muscular dystrophy—and probably some other myopathies as well—may not be 'primary' disorders of muscle, as is at present believed, but are associated with an aberration within the nervous system.

This will be discussed from three aspects, namely those features of muscular dystrophy which cannot be explained on a purely 'muscle' basis; experimental work to illustrate the remarkable influence of the nervous system on skeletal muscle—not only on its contractile properties but also on its structure and function; and thirdly the possible role of the nervous system in the genesis of pathological changes within the muscle.

CLINICO-PATHOLOGICAL ASPECTS

Intellectual impairment in muscular dystrophy

Duchenne's first case (1861) was mentally retarded, and he suggested the name 'paraplegie hypertrophique de l'enfance de cause cerebralé'. In his subsequent series of 13 cases, 5 were retarded and he was less convinced of the cerebral origin of the muscular disorder and called it 'paralysie musculaire pseudohypertrophique' (Duchenne, 1872). Although the association with intellectual retardation has been doubted by some authors (Walton & Nattrass, 1954) or ascribed to the physical handicap and lack of educational opportunity (Morrow & Cohen, 1954), others have been more convinced of its significance (Giannini & Marcheschi, 1959; Allen & Rodgin, 1960; Worden & Vignos, 1962; Dubowitz, 1965a; Zellweger & Niedermeyer, 1965).

There are two strong arguments against the mental retardation being secondary to the physical handicap. One does not see intellectual impairment in patients with proximal neurogenic atrophies of comparable severity; and the intellectual impairment has been shown to antedate the onset of motor weakness in cases diagnosed in the 'preclinical' stage of muscular dystrophy (Dubowitz, 1965a).

It is of interest that, in contrast to the dystrophic process, the intellectual retardation is not progressive. Although the intelligence varies widely from patient to patient and ranges from an I.Q. of below 40 at one extreme to above 120 at the other, there is concordance within an affected family.

This is well illustrated in a number of families I have studied within one large pedigree (Fig. 1). All the affected boys showed a similar marked degree of intellectual impairment, while the unaffected sibs were all of normal intelligence.

It is difficult to explain why only a proportion of children with muscular dystrophy of the Duchenne Type have associated mental retardation, while perhaps 50 per cent or more, with a similar degree of muscle weakness, have normal intelligence. One possibility is that there can be a wide variation in the severity, as with many inborn errors of metabolism, such as phenylketonuria. An alternative explanation is that there may be different disease entities with a different metabolic defect, perhaps on the same chain of reactions, producing a similar myopathy but with a difference in the intellectual involvement. A similar explanation may account for the absence of intellectual impairment in other forms of muscular dystrophy, such as the facioscapulohumeral and limb girdle varieties.

Electroencephalographic (EEG) abnormality in muscular dystrophy

Intellectual impairment is not the only central nervous system manifestation which has been reported in muscular dystrophy. Consistent abnormalities in the EEG, in the form of 14 and 6 per second positive spikes, have been observed in children with muscular dystrophy, with an incidence ranging from about 30 to 70 per cent in different series (Winfield, Britt & Raskind, 1958; Perlstein, Gibbs, Gibbs & Stein, 1960; and Zellweger & Neidermeyer, 1965). In contrast Barwick, Osselton & Walton (1965) found no significant incidence of abnormality compared with controls.

The significance of the EEG changes in muscular dystrophy is difficult to assess. Although Gibbs & Gibbs (1951) regarded positive spiking as evidence of thalamic-hypothalamic epilepsy, it has since been shown that 14 and 6 per second positive spikes are rarely seen in definite epileptic states but are more common in certain 'borderland' areas of epilepsy such as migrainous states, syncope, paroxysmal abdominal pain, and other autonomic dysfunctions (Presthus, Refsum, Skulstad & Ostensjoe, 1956; Poser & Ziegler, 1958). Zellweger & Neidermeyer (1965) found no correlation between the intellectual impairment and the EEG abnormality in their patients.

Neuropathological changes in muscular dystrophy

The absence of any apparent abnormality in the central nervous system was noted in the first autopsy reports on muscular dystrophy (Merjon, 1852; Eulenburg & Cohnheim, 1866) and this conclusion has been supported by subsequent investigations (Adams, Denny-Brown & Pearson, 1962).

However, in a recent study of seven cases of Duchenne dystrophy, collected from the autopsy files of the Massachusetts General Hospital

C

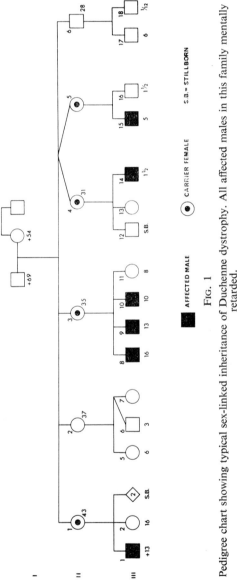

FIG. 1

Pedigree chart showing typical sex-linked inheritance of Duchenne dystrophy. All affected males in this family mentally retarded.

since 1896, Rosman and Kakulas (1966) observed abnormalities in the cerebral hemispheres of all three cases with associated intellectual impairment, but in none of the remaining four who were said to have normal intelligence. There were microscopic heterotopias with large numbers of neurones in the subcortical and deeper layers of the cerebral white matter. They ascribed these changes to a disorder of cortical development during foetal life with a disturbance of the normal neuronal migration. This is an interesting observation and needs further prospective study.

Pseudohypertrophy

This classical feature of muscular dystrophy, occurring most frequently in the Duchenne type, is dependent on an intact nerve supply. Children

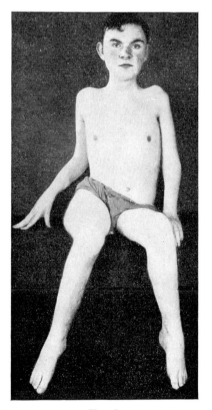

Fig. 2

Poliomyelitis after muscular dystrophy with atrophy of left deltoid and right calf.

who develop poliomyelitis subsequent to muscular dystrophy lose the pseudohypertrophy in the affected muscles (Fig. 2).

EXPERIMENTAL STUDIES

Having reviewed some of the manifestations of muscular dystrophy which implicate the central nervous system, I would like to discuss the evidence from experimental work in animals which suggests a nervous influence on normal muscle and has pathological implications.

In animals, physiologists have long recognized the presence of different muscles with slow or fast speeds of contraction. These correlate with the red and white muscles respectively of the early anatomists. The slow muscle is capable of sustained activity and depends on oxidative enzymes of the Krebs cycle for its energy, while the fast muscle, adapted for rapid bursts of unsustained activity, depends on anaerobic glycolysis.

By histochemical techniques one can characterize individual muscle fibres within a muscle on the basis of their enzyme activities (Dubowitz & Pearse, 1960a). Type 1 fibres are rich in oxidative enzymes and poor in phosphorylase and correspond to red or slow muscle, while type 2 fibres, rich in phosphorylase and poor in oxidative enzymes, correspond to fast or white muscle. There are also intermediate fibres. In humans all muscles are a mixture of histochemical fibre types but the proportion of these varies in different muscles (Fig. 3).

FIG. 3

Normal human deltoid muscle showing checkerboard of type 1 (strongly reacting) and type 2 fibres.
Reduced NAD—tetrazolium oxidoreductase
$(NADH_2) \times 200$.

In foetal muscle the fibres are initially undifferentiated in both animals and humans and become differentiated into the adult types in the course of development (Dubowitz, 1965 b,c). The differentiation probably coincides with the full innervation of the fibres and maturation of the motor end-plates.

Buller, Eccles & Eccles (1960b) set out to demonstrate that the contractile properties of fast and slow muscles are determined by the nervous system. In an elegant series of experiments they showed that when the nerve to the slow soleus muscle is cross-united with the nerve to the fast flexor digitorum longus (FDL) in the cat, the soleus after reinnervation becomes 'fast' in its contractile properties while the FDL becomes 'slow'. They postulated that this influence was chemical in nature and came from the central nervous system via the anterior horn cells and axons, traversed the neuromuscular junction and spread into the muscle fibres. They also demonstrated that all muscle in the cat is slow at birth and that the potentially fast muscle gradually acquires its different contractile properties (Buller, Eccles & Eccles, 1960a). They postulated that this maturation was under the same chemical influence of the nervous system.

In a series of experiments on newborn and full grown cats and rabbits we have studied the effects of cross-innervation not only on the contractile properties but also on the histochemical pattern of the muscle. The physiological changes produced were similar to those recorded by Buller, Eccles & Eccles. In addition there were striking changes in the histochemical pattern of the muscle fibres (Dubowitz & Newman, 1967; Dubowitz, 1967b).

Normally the soleus is composed entirely of histochemical type 1 fibres (Fig. 4) while the FDL contains predominantly type 2 fibres and small groups of type 1 or intermediate fibres (Fig. 5). Following cross-union the FDL showed large areas composed uniformly of type 1 fibres and indistinguishable from normal soleus muscle (Fig. 6). The soleus, conversely, showed areas of type 2 fibres similar to those of normal FDL. This suggests that not only the contractile properties but also the enzymic pattern of the muscle fibres is controlled by the type of innervation of the muscle.

There have been a number of additional observations on the effects of cross-innervation on the chemistry of the muscle. Drahota & Gutmann (1963) found an increase in the potassium and glycogen content of the soleus after cross-innervation by the nerve to flexor digitorum longus but no corresponding change in the cross-innervated flexor digitorum longus muscle. Recently McPherson & Takunaga (1967) have shown a change in myoglobin content of the slow and fast muscles after cross-innervation.

In the course of this study a number of striking pathological changes within the muscle fibres were observed during the early phases of re-innervation (Dubowitz, 1967a). The most frequent were 'snake coil' fibres which

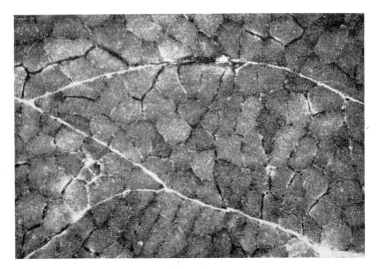

FIG. 4
Normal cat soleus showing uniformity of enzymic
activity.
NADH$_2$ × 110.

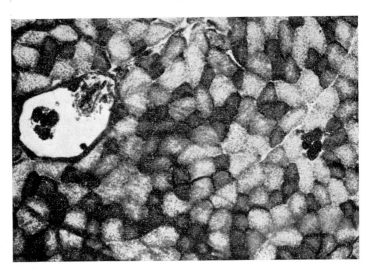

FIG. 5
Normal cat flexor digitorum longus. Note larger
weakly-reacting type 2 fibres, smaller type 1 fibres and
intermediate fibres.
NADH$_2$ × 110.

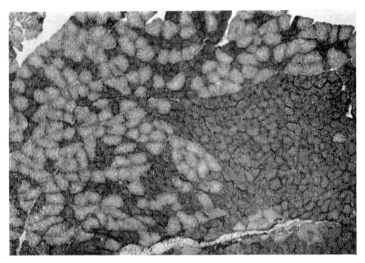

FIG. 6

Cat flexor digitorum longus, cross-innervated, showing large area of type 1 fibres similar to normal
soleus.

NADH$_2$ × 44.

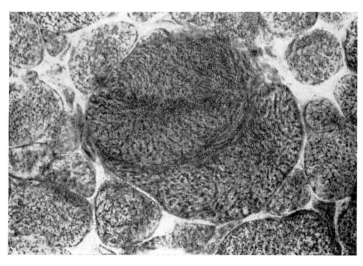

FIG. 7

Rabbit flexor digitorum longus showing coil fibre
during reinnervation.

NADH$_2$ × 440.

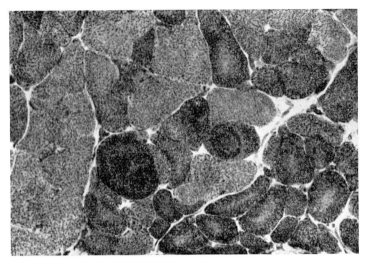

FIG. 8
Rabbit flexor digitorum longus showing variation in
fibre size, coil fibres and core fibres, with central
area devoid of enzyme activity.
NADH$_2$ × 176.

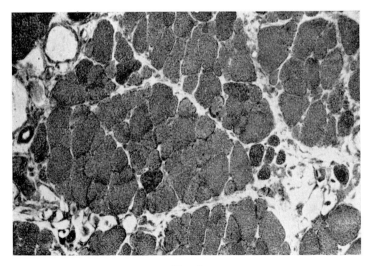

FIG. 9
Rabbit soleus showing 'myopathic' pattern of vary-
ing fibre size, during reinnervation.
NADH$_2$ × 110.

had various bizarre shapes (Fig. 7) and 'core' fibres in which a central core was devoid of enzyme activity (Fig. 8). Occasional fibres showed 'ringbinden' with a peripheral longitudinal band of muscle fibrils around the transverse section of a muscle fibre. There were also many giant fibres, vacuolated fibres, and in some bundles, a random variation in size of fibres comparable with a 'myopathic' pattern (Fig. 9). These clearly illustrate the wide range of pathological changes that can occur in the process of reinnervation of the muscle fibre.

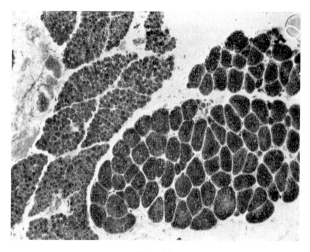

FIG. 10
Proximal neurogenic muscular atrophy of mild type, aged 2 years. Quadriceps. Atrophic fibres composed of type 1 and type 2 fibres; large fibres all type 1 and also show some central cores.
NADH₂ × 100.

CLINICAL CORRELATIONS

If the fibre type is dependent on the nervous system, it now becomes easy to understand some earlier observations in various pathological states. In neurogenic atrophy of muscle there is a uniform 'group' atrophy of large numbers of fibres interspersed with isolated, or groups of, normal-sized or large fibres. The latter were frequently of one histochemical type only (Fig. 10) (Dubowitz & Pearse, 1961; Fenichel & Engel, 1963; Dubowitz, 1966). If they were normal bundles of fibres, one would expect a checkerboard pattern as in normal muscle. It now seems likely that they are reinnervated muscle fibres and presumably result from the sprouting of surviving nerve fibres of one histochemical type.

In some advanced cases of muscular dystrophy we observed a similar phenomenon (Dubowitz & Pearse, 1961). Many of the abnormally large fibres tended to correspond to one enzymic type (type 2), while the small atrophic fibres tended to be predominantly of the other type. This may have a similar basis to the neurogenic atrophies.

Absence of the differentiation of muscle into the constituent histo-chemical types probably represents an abnormality of the normal process of maturation of muscle. This has been observed on a number of occasions. In a case of central core disease all the fibres showed a uniform enzyme activity (Dubowitz & Pearse, 1960b), while in another case (Dubowitz & Platts, 1965) only type 1 fibres contained cores. It is of interest that in addition to the possible influence of the nervous system on the uniformity of fibre type, the cores themselves can occur during experimental reinner-vation.

Engel (1961, 1962) has shown that in long-standing neurogenic atrophies in man the fibres frequently showed central cores devoid of enzyme activity, similar to those observed in hereditary central core disease of muscle. He looked upon these as a sign of denervation but from our experimental studies it seems more likely that they occur as a result of reinnervation of the muscle. It is also possible that hereditary central core disease, one of the 'congenital non-progressive myopathies' (Shy & Magee, 1956) may itself not be a myopathy but represent an abnormality in development under nervous influence.

In the early stages of muscular dystrophy one observes individual muscle fibres which do not show the normal reciprocity of different enzymes but have a uniform activity of the various enzyme systems comparable to foetal muscle. This may represent a delayed maturation of some muscle fibres. It is of interest to compare this with the hereditary muscular dys-trophy of the chick which affects predominantly the pectoral muscles. It has been observed that in chick dystrophy there is a delay in the normal differentiation of the fibres into the mature histochemical fibre types and that this selectively involves the type 2 fibre (Cosmos, 1966). This raises the question as to whether some factor in the process of normal maturation of foetal muscle may be responsible for the onset of the dystrophic process. Other observations, such as the occurrence in dystrophic muscle of foetal myoglobin (Perkoff, 1964) and a foetal pattern of the isoenzymes of lactic dehydrogenase (Dreyfus, Demos, Schapira & Schapira, 1962), may also be important in this context.

In 1879 Gowers wrote of muscular dystrophy:

'This disease is one of the most interesting and at the same time most sad of all those with which we have to deal; interesting on account of its peculiar features and mysterious nature; sad on account of our power-lessness to influence its course'.

Its nature is as much a mystery to us today as it was to Gowers nearly a century ago. Perhaps we shall have a little more insight into the disease in the future if we set our sights beyond the muscle itself and look into the striking influence of the nervous system on muscle, not only in its pathology but also in its very structure and function.

REFERENCES

ADAMS, R. D., DENNY-BROWN, D., & PEARSON, C. M. (1962). *Diseases of Muscle. A Study in Pathology.* 2nd Ed. p. 360. New York: Harper.
ALLEN, J. D. & RODGIN, D. W. (1960). *Am. J. Dis. Child.* **100**, 208.
BARWICK, D. D., OSSELTON, J. W., & WALTON, J. N. (1965). *J. Neurol. Neurosurg. Psychiat.* **28**, 109.
BULLER, A. J., ECCLES, J. C., & ECCLES, R. M. (1960*a*). *J. Physiol.* **150**, 399.
BULLER, A. J., ECCLES, J. C., & ECCLES, R. M. (1960*b*). *J. Physiol.* **150**, 417.
COSMOS, E. (1966). *Devl. Biol.* **13**, 103.
DRAHOTA, Z. & GUTMANN, E. (1963). In *The Effects of Use and Disuse on Neuromuscular Functions.* Ed. Gutmann, E. and Hnik, P. p. 143. Prague: Czechoslovak Academy of Science.
DREYFUS, J. C., DEMOS, J. SCHAPIRA, F., & SCHAPIRA, G. (1962). *C. r. hebd. Seanc. Acad. Sci. Paris* **254**, 4384.
DUBOWITZ, V. (1965*a*). *Archs Dis. Childh.* **40**, 296.
DUBOWITZ, V. (1965*b*). *J. Neurol. Neurosurg. Psychiat.* **28**, 516.
DUBOWITZ, V. (1965*c*). *J. Neurol. Neurosurg. Psychiat.* **28**, 519.
DUBOWITZ, V. (1966). *J. Neurol. Neurosurg. Psychiat.* **29**, 23.
DUBOWITZ, V. (1967*a*). *J. Neurol. Neurosurg. Psychiat.* **30**, 99.
DUBOWITZ, V. (1967*b*). *J. Physiol.* **193**, 481.
DUBOWITZ, V. & NEWMAN, D. L. (1967). *Nature, Lond.* **214**, 840.
DUBOWITZ, V. & PEARSE, A. G. E. (1960*a*). *Nature, Lond.* **185**, 701.
DUBOWITZ, V. & PEARSE, A. G. E. (1960*b*). *Lancet* **2**, 23.
DUBOWITZ, V. & PEARSE, A. G. E. (1961). *J. Path. Bact.* **81**, 365.
DUBOWITZ, V. & PLATTS, M. (1965). *J. Neurol. Neurosurg. Psychiat.* **28**, 432.
DUCHENNE, G. B. (1861). *De l'Electrisation Localisée et son Application à la Pathologie et à la Therapéutique.* 2nd ed. Paris: Bailliere.
DUCHENNE, G. B. (1872). *De l'Electrisation Localisée et son Application à la Pathologie et à la Therapéutique.* 3rd ed. Paris, Bailliere.
ENGEL, W. K. (1961). *Nature, Lond.* **191**, 389.
ENGEL, W. K. (1962). *Neurology, Minneap.* **12**, 778.
EULENBURG, A. VON & COHNHEIM, R. (1866). *Verh. berl. med. Ges.* **191**, 210.
FENICHEL, G. M. & ENGEL, W. K. (1963). *Neurology, Minneap.* **13**, 1059.
GIANNINI, C. & MARCHESCHI, M. (1959). *Sist. nerv.* **6**, 461.
GIBBS, E. & GIBBS, F. (1951). *Neurology, Minneap.* **1**, 136.
GOWERS, W. R. (1879). *Pseudo-hypertrophic Muscular Paralysis. A Clinical Lecture.* London: Churchill.
MCPHERSON, A. & TOKUNAGA, J. (1967). *J. Physiol., Lond.* **188**, 121.
MERYON, E. (1852). *Med.-chir. Trans.* **17**, 73.
MORROW, R. S. & COHEN, J. (1954). *J. Child Psychiat.* **3**, 70.
PERKOFF, G. T. (1964). *New Engl. J. Med.* **270**, 263.
PERLSTEIN, N. A., GIBBS, F. A., GIBBS, E. L., & STEIN, M. D. (1960). *J. Am. Med. Ass.* **173**, 1329.
POSER, C. M. & ZIEGLER, D. (1958). *Neurology Minneap.* **8**, 903.
PRESTHUS, J., REFSUM, S., SKULSTAD, A. & OSTENSJOE, S. (1956). *Acta psychiat. neurol. scand.* **31**, 166.
ROSMAN, N. P. & KAKULAS, B. A. (1966). *Brain,* **89**, 769.
SHY, G. M. & MAGEE, K. R. (1956). *Brain* **79**, 610.
WALTON, J. N. & NATTRESS, F. J. (1954). *Brain* **77**, 169.
WINFIELD, D. L., BRITT, L. P., & RASKIND, R. (1958). *Sth. Med. J. Nashville,* **51**, 1251.
WORDEN, D. K. & VIGNOS, P. J. (1962). *Pediatrics, Springfield* **29**, 968.
ZELLWEGER, H. & NIEDERMEYER, E. (1965). *Anns paediat.* **205**, 25.

DISCUSSION OF PRESENTATIONS BY
DR. WALTON, DR. PENNINGTON AND DR. DUBOWITZ

Crome (Carshalton). Would the speakers please comment on the 'floppy baby' syndrome? It may be very difficult to diagnose muscular dystrophy in these patients.

Walton. I agree that the floppy baby may present a very difficult problem. Those most severely floppy and who remain so for months after birth have, on occasions, turned out to have Werdnig Hoffman disease. Another group of these infants turned out to have mental deficiency and spastic diplegia. A further group where muscle appears to be primarily involved had very profound muscle weakness. These patients never stand, they never walk and many, but not all, have severe contractures. Serum creatine kinase is slightly raised—electromyography shows severe myopathy. Muscle biopsy shows more severe changes. In congenital muscular dystrophy the picture histologically is not very different from other forms of muscular dystrophy. In benign congenital hypotonia the serum enzymes are normal, these children do walk but later than usual. They remain rather hypotonic and muscle biopsy shows very minor non-specific changes. We have not found any specific histological pattern in these cases but they can be distinguished. Occasionally a floppy baby may turn out to have myotonic dystrophy. One such patient was observed from birth and was proved at 4 years to have myotonic dystrophy. Incidentally, we recently had another such patient and on examination of the mother it was established that she too had clear-cut myotonic dystrophy.

Dubowitz. I too have seen this. I think these babies often look very much like the mother—expressionless face, mouth tending to be half open. I would like to know what advice should be given to parents starting a family or having further children?

Gardener-Medwin (Newcastle). I would advise them not to have a family.

Bower (Oxford). I would like to ask Dr. Walton his opinion on the relationship between the Kugelberg-Welander syndrome and Werdnig Hoffman disease?

Walton. I do not believe that the Kugelberg-Welander syndrome can be identified as a specific syndrome. If you look at cases with classical Wernig-Hoffman in infancy and follow them for a number of years, quite a few follow a classical course and die within a year or two helplessly paralysed. In quite a number of cases however, the disease seems to stop, leaving marked paralysis but quite a few of these patients live. In two families which I have seen, one affected sib ran a classical course and the other showed a late-onset of muscle weakness and ran a benign course. I feel that the syndrome despite the late onset and benign course is related to Werdnig-Hoffman disease.

Dubowitz. Would Dr. Pennington comment on the iso-enzymes of creatine kinase in relationship to muscle and brain?

Pennington. There is some discrepancy in the data published but there are two basic isoenzymes—muscle units called M and brain units called B. Normally adult muscle contains nearly all MM with a small amount of BB whereas brain contains largely BB. Foetal muscle contains a reduced amount of MM and relatively more BB. This was also found in dystrophic muscle. When the serum creatine kinase was looked at in head injuries and strokes, it was expected that BB would be found whereas MM was found and it seemed to indicate that this enzyme was leaking out of the muscle and not the brain.

Raine (Birmingham). Which of the 3 investigations—electromyography, muscle biopsy, serum creatine kinase would have the greatest diagnostic efficiency?

Walton. Where all three tests were done, in my experience the serum creatine kinase was the best.

Dickenson (Leeds). Was there any correlation between muscle biopsy and creatine kinase levels?

Walton. We found no evidence that the individuals with the highest serum creatine kinase level were more likely to have greater histological abnormality.

Burns (Wolverley). Were completely negative results obtained in normal controls or were there any false positives?

Walton. Tests were certainly carried out against normal controls and no false positives were found.

Pennington. It has been reported that very violent exercise can produce false positives but we have never found this and it would be my view that the exercise would have to be very violent indeed.

Stern (Carshalton). I found Dr. Dubowitz's paper very interesting, stimulating and provocative and he has done us a great service in drawing our attention to the possible role of the nervous system in muscular dystrophy. I would certainly agree that structural changes in the brain must be looked for in cases of muscular dystrophy but very subtle measures would have to be undertaken. Also one has to be very careful when assessing the I.Q. of children with muscular dystrophy. The results may be affected even in the pre-clinical state of the disease. Would Dr. Dubowitz have second thoughts on the points he made in his paper regarding this?

Dubowitz. On reflection I agree with my first thoughts.

Walton. It is our experience that intelligence is affected especially in Duchenne type muscular dystrophy and the I.Q. is significantly lower in this type when compared with other types of muscular dystrophy. Studies of the I.Q. in Duchenne type muscular dystrophy and spinal muscular atrophy are currently being carried out in Newcastle Upon Tyne.

SKELETAL MUSCLE GLYCOGENOSES OTHER THAN TYPE II

Brian McArdle*

THE current position with regard to the various types of glycogenosis is briefly indicated in Fig. 1 which shows the relevant stages in glycogen synthesis and breakdown in muscle, the enzymatic deficiency or deficiencies where these are known, and the disease types marked at the appropriate points. The classification is basically that of Cori (1957) though they will not be taken in numerical order.

PATHWAYS OF GLYCOGEN METABOLISM IN MUSCLE

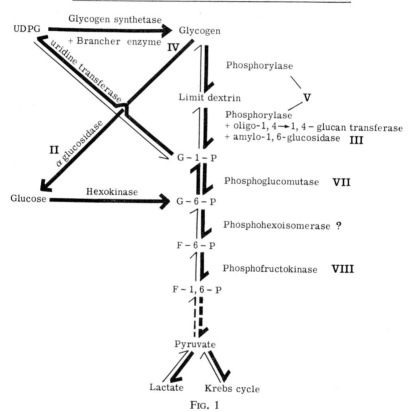

Fig. 1

Where a defect of an enzyme or enzyme system is known to occur it is followed by the Type number (Cori, 1956) of the glycogenosis.

* External Scientific Staff of Medical Research Council.

MUSCLE GLYCOGENOSES OTHER THAN TYPE V

Type I is missing from Table I as there is no glucose-6-phosphatase in muscle. Type II, Pompe's disease, is due to deficiency of the lysosomal a-1, 4-glucosidase (acid maltase) and will be dealt with by Dr. Hudgson in the following paper. The very rare Type IV (Andersen, 1956, Sidbury, Mason, Burns & Ruebner, 1962) occurring in small infants, affects muscles in addition to liver, kidneys, heart and other tissues, but the muscle involvement contributes little to the clinical picture of cirrhosis and liver failure and need not concern us further. Biochemically though, it is of interest since it seems very likely that it is due to the absence of amylo-1, 4 1,6-transglucosidase—the "brancher enzyme"—resulting in abnormal glycogen molecules having relatively long chains of a-1, 4-linked glucosyl units.

In Type III glycogenosis (Forbes, 1953; Cori, 1957) the glycogen is also abnormal but the structure is quite different from Type IV, approximating to the limit dextrin formed by the action of phosphorylase on glycogen, having short outer chains and a higher percentage of end groups. It is for this reason that it is sometimes called "limit dextrinosis". It has been shown (Illingworth, Cori & Cori, 1956) to be due to a deficiency of amylo-1, 6-glucosidase—the 'debrancher enzyme'. The condition can affect liver, muscle and heart either separately or in varying combination depending on the organs in which the enzyme is deficient. Very low levels of the enzyme in this disease have been found in leucocytes (Williams, Kendig & Field, 1963) and raised levels of glycogen in erythrocytes (Sidbury, Gitzelmann & Fisher, 1961). It is rare for the presenting symptoms to stem from the muscles, though in infancy they may be hypotonic—the clinical picture being rather like that of Type II though with a better prognosis. However, Oliner, Schulman & Larner (1961) have described an unusual case of a man aged 50 years having a myopathy with absent or minimal amylo-1, 6-glucosidase in muscle and liver. As in the other muscle glycogenoses due to known deficiencies of the anaerobic glycogenolytic enzymes there was no rise of blood lactate following the ischaemic work test and, interestingly, only a minimal rise in two of his four children. Two further adult patients with muscle involvement have been reported (Hatcher, Sidbury & Heyman, 1964).

Only one case of Type VII glycogenosis appears to have been described. This was a 4 year old boy described by Thomson, Maclaurin & Prineas (1963) with a mild myopathy, an abnormal gait due to a marked and permanent contracture of his calves and having only a slight rise in blood lactate after ischaemic exercise. Biopsied muscles contained a very considerable amount of glycogen both histologically and biochemically (3·7 to 11·3 g./100 g. tissue). The structure of the glycogen was normal and since degradation of glucose-l-phosphate to lactate on anaerobic glycolysis was only about one fifth of that from glucose-6-phosphate or fructose-1, 6-

diphosphate, it was concluded that the defect lay at the level of phosphoglucomutase.

A child of 2½ years with massive deposits of glycogen of normal structure
in his muscles reported by di Sant Agnese, Andersen & Metcalf (1962)
is difficult to fit into any group. Clinically, there was hypotonia, a 'splayed
gait' and a palatal palsy that caused severe feeding difficulties and frequent
bounts of pneumonia. The heart and liver were not enlarged.

Two brothers complaining of pain occurring some hours after moderately
heavy exercise were studied by Satoyoshi & Kowa (1965). The blood lactate
did not rise after ischaemic exercise but did so when this followed ingestion
of fructose. There was little or no increase in muscle glycogen, but on
anaerobic glycolysis a block was found at the level of hexoseisomerase
though substrates below this level were normally degraded to lactate.
However, the activity of hexoseisomerase proved to be normal on direct
estimation as did that of phosphorylase and phosphoglucomutase. On the
other hand phosphofructokinase activity was found decreased by about
50%. The authors considered some form of inhibition as the most likely
explanation of this confusing picture.

A new glycogen storage disease of muscle which will presumably be
called Type VIII has been described in three members of a single family by
Tarui, Okuno, Okura, Tanaka, Suda & Nishikawa (1965) in whom they
were able to demonstrate a clearcut deficiency of phosphofructokinase. A
further case has been more recently described by Layzer, Rowland &
Ranney (1967). The clinical, pathological and other features of this condition are (as might be expected) so strikingly similar to that found in phosphorylase deficiency of muscle, that it seems likely that, with a few exceptions, what applies to one applies to the other. The condition therefore will
not be given separate consideration, since the remainder of the paper will
be concerned with phosphorylase deficiency of muscle.

Type V Glycogenosis

Like many of the more interesting inborn errors of metabolism, Type V
glycogenosis (phosphorylase deficiency myopathy, or McArdle's disease
(McArdle, 1951)) is a rare disease—I have had to wait 17 years for a
second case and only 31 cases have been described in the literature. None
the less it is the most frequent cause of glycogenosis in adults. As its symptoms and signs are likely to be common to any disease (described, as in
phosphofructokinase deficiency, or yet to be described) due to an absolute
deficiency of any enzyme in the direct pathway of anaerobic glycolysis, I
propose to describe the condition in some detail illustrating it from my own
two cases.

The main complaint is of pain on exercise, usually in the calves and
thighs on hurrying or walking up hills. The pain though, is not confined to

the lower limbs but occurs in any muscle on moderate or severe exercise, occurring even in the jaw muscles on vigorous or prolonged chewing. The pain disappears within a few minutes on resting but if the exercise is continued the dull pain becomes more intense, lasts longer on resting, and is accompanied by stiffness and weakness of the affected muscles. The pattern is seen best, perhaps, in the upper limbs—a characteristic story being that on carrying a heavy weight with both hands, the patient may have to drop or put down the weight because of the pain and may then be unable to straighten his flexed fingers for some minutes. Full extension may not be possible for 5 to 20 mins. depending on how long the weight was carried. The stiffness is manifested in the legs by the development of a 'stiff-legged' gait, and in my second patient could become so severe that he was quite unable to bend his knees. This association of pain and stiffness— or even the pain alone—is often described in the literature as a 'cramp'—a confusing term, since the pain and later the stiffness build up and then diminish gradually.

Dyspnoea, palpitations and a greatly increased heart rate become noticeable if even moderate exercise such as climbing stairs is persisted in after the development of pain. None the less a number of the patients give a story of 'second wind'. (Pearson, Rimer & Mommaerts, 1961). This only occurs with mild exercise. Pain may develop whilst walking at a moderate pace on the flat, but may then disappear even though the exercise is continued, and they may then find they are able to continue almost indefinitely at the same or even a slightly increased pace. They also notice that exercising after a long period is especially liable to give rise to pain, whilst a period of 'limbering up' increases their exercise tolerance.

An intriguing symptom noted by both patients, but not referred to in most of the other papers, has been an abnormally increased appetite, especially after exercise.

Myoglobinuria occurs at some time in a considerable number of these patients, but usually only on two or three occasions. It had not occurred in my original case nor has it been noticed in the eighteen years of follow up, but my second patient has noted what was almost certainly transient myoglobinuria on two, possibly three occasions. This second patient also finds that if for any reason he has to continue with vigorous exercise despite pain and increasing stiffness, the muscles involved will, some hours later, have become sore, tender, swollen and weak and it may be two or three days before these symptoms subside. This is perhaps more likely to occur in his arm and trunk muscles and it may not be without significance that his arm and trunk muscles are noticeably weaker and less well developed than those of his legs.

The disease would appear to occur predominantly in males. Of the 31 cases described in the literature, plus my second case (in the process of being written up) only 6 have been female, and in all except one the propo-situs was male. However, this sex difference may be more apparent than real since the male is more likely to seek medical advice for muscle pain on exertion and more likely perhaps, to be more fully investigated. In the six families with more than one member affected there were ten males and six females. It is likely, therefore, that the sex distribution is not as marked as as the figures would seem to indicate.

As a rule the diagnosis has been made in the latter half of the second or during the third decade with the symptoms dating from childhood, but Engel, Eyerman & Williams (1963) have described a 'late onset type' in a brother and sister who did not develop symptoms until their fiftieth year. The sister aged 52—had had no pain on exertion but had progressive weakness, some wasting, and profound muscular fatigue on exertion. She had no phosphorylase in her muscles, but her brother who suffered from severe aching and painful 'cramps' some hours after exercise, had only a partial deficiency of phosphorylase in his muscles. It would seem as though this family constitutes a subgroup on their own.

On routine clinical examination the majority of the patients seem to be completely normal, though a small number may show some myopathic wasting. Moderately vigorous exercise however leads not only to pain, alterations in gait, and early fatigue, but also to abnormally increased ventilation and pulse rates. I usually try to produce some shortening of the forearm muscles. This characteristic feature of the condition is best elicited by asking the patient to work on a grip ergometer or squeeze a sphygmomanometer bulb with the circulation to the forearm occluded by a sphygmomanometer cuff inflated to 200 mm. of Hg.—or higher if necessary. The ischaemic exercise is continued until stopped by pain or fatigue. At this point and when the circulation is restored the patient is likely to show considerable limitation of extension of his fingers, it may be for several minutes, and often, shows some degree of ulnar deviation. I have been careful to use the phrase 'shortening of muscle' and avoid the terms spasm, contraction or cramp since electromyography of the shortened forearm flexors show the muscle to be electrically silent, that is, the muscle is in a state of physiological 'contracture'. (McArdle, 1951; Rowland, Lovelace, Schotland, Araki & Carmel, 1966).

It is not generally appreciated that it is possible to induce this almost diagnostic shortening of muscle more easily and with less pain to the patient when the work load on the ergometer is heavy or when there is a consider-able resistance to the outflow of air from the sphygmomanometer bulb.

The next step in establishing the diagnosis consists of measuring the venous blood lactate following release of the circulation after a period of ischaemic exercise. Ischaemic exercise is used since ordinary exercise would have to be of sufficient intensity to produce an adequate rise in blood lactate in normal fit young men and it is probable that some patients would be unable to exercise at this pace.

The ischaemic exercise test is best done with a standard amount of work on a suitable ergometer, but a sphygmomanometer bulb is frequently used. In the absence of oxygen, glycogen broken down by exercising normal muscles is converted to lactate and a considerable rise in blood lactate occurs following restoration of the circulation. This is usually of the order of 10 to 30 mg./100 ml. and remains elevated (though falling) for the ensuing 20 to 30 mins. In cases of phosphorylase deficiency however, glycogen cannot be broken down and there is no increase in the venous blood lactate—if anything there is a tendency for the level of blood lactate to fall. In performing the test it is important that the blood should be coming from the exercised muscles and not from the hands, which may be vasodilated and contributing arterialized blood without increase in lactate. Such admixture can be prevented by inflating a wrist cuff above the systolic pressure before releasing the upper arm cuff and 30 secs. before any later blood samples.

This test has proved very useful in the screening of patients with pain on exercise or with myoglobinuria, but it should be emphasized that it merely indicates a block in the breakdown of glycogen to lactic acid, a block that theoretically might be due to a number of enzyme defects, and in fact is known to be caused by phosphofructokinase deficiency (Tarui et al., 1965) and by partial defects at the level of phosphoglucomutase (Thompson, Maclaurin & Prineas, 1963) and phosphohexoisomerase (Satoyoshi & Kowa, 1965).

It seems likely that in muscle phosphofructokinase deficiency, an ancillary method of diagnosis, may well be the estimation in red cells of phosphofructokinase isoenzymes. In a case of muscle phosphofructokinase deficiency, Layzer, Rowland & Ranney (1967), have found the particular isoenzyme characteristic of muscle absent also in red cells, whereas that typical of liver was present in normal amount. In their original cases Tarui et al., had earlier found the (total) phosphofructokinase activity to be reduced.

Differential Diagnosis

Any condition that causes pain in muscles during and/or shortly after exercise must enter into the differential diagnosis of those enzyme deficiencies causing a block in muscle glycogenolysis. The various vascular and blood disorders giving rise to intermittent claudication are obvious possibilities, but these in general are easy to exclude and in practice I have rarely been referred a case as a possible example of phosphorylase deficiency. Those referred I have thought to be examples either of polymyositis, of the paramyotonia congenita-hyperkalaemic periodic paralysis group, of the benign Duchenne myopathy with developing contractures in the calves, of frequent true cramps when especially related to exercise or posture, and even of varicose veins. A glycogenolytic block must also be excluded in most types of myoglobinuria and, in some, clinical differentiation can be very difficult.

The points I have thought most helpful in diagnosis have been the early age of onset, the fact that all muscles are affected, the stiffness and shortening of the muscles, and often, the disproportionate dyspnoea and rapid heart action. The diagnosis becomes the more probable if, in addition, there is a history of myoglobinuria on one or more occasions. Where there is any doubt as to the diagnosis the lactate response to ischaemic exercise can be most helpful, though unfortunately not infallible.

There are other very rare conditions which enter into the differential diagnosis such as the megaconial myopathy recently described by Shy, Gonatas & Perez (1966), and the familial non-progressive myopathy with muscle cramps after exercise reported by Bethlem, van Gool, Hülsmann & Meijer (1966). But these, like phosphorylase deficiency itself, should be kept in proper perspective, at the very back of one's mind.

In all too many cases that I have been referred I have been unable to make a definite diagnosis, though able to exclude a block in glycogenolysis. There is a group of these patients in whom the pain on exercise is probably determined by psychological factors. However, there have been a number where there has been no reason to suppose there is any psychological element, but in whom it has not been possible to obtain any objective evidence of muscle disease. It is a field requiring further investigation.

Muscle Biochemistry

The phosphorylase stage in glycogen breakdown is especially important as it is an enzyme which controls, according to the degree of its activation, the rate of glycogenolysis. There are a number of enzymes concerned with the activation of phorphorylase and it is conceivable that a deficiency of one or more of these might have a similar effect to a deficiency of phosphorylase itself.

None the less the activities of most of these other enzymes concerned with phosphorylase interconversions were explored and found normal by Schmid & Mahler (1959) and Mommaerts, Illingworth, Pearson, Guillory & Seraydarian (1959) that phosphorylase activity was deficient in this condition. Many of the later workers have not been so scrupulous in this respect, but it seems that this may not now be so necessary, for it is likely that control of glycogenolysis by phosphorylase does not rest solely on the conversion, by phosphorylase b kinase, of the inactive phosphorylase b to the active 'a' form. Lyon & Porter (1963) have described an inbred strain of apparently normal mice in whom both phosphorylase a and phosphorylase b kinase were almost absent in skeletal muscle. Despite this, normal increased glycogenolysis followed exercise and adrenaline administration. It seems likely also that phosphorylase b can be activated other than by conversion to the 'a' form.

Since the diagnosis at the time of taking the muscle biopsy is only presumptive, it is convenient not only to measure phosphorylase activity by a standard specific method, but also to determine the overall ability of the muscle to degrade endogenous glycogen and added substrates to lactate. If there is a block in glycolysis, not only is the initial level of lactate in the muscle before incubation very low but there is no further rise in lactate when substrates above the level of the block are added. When substrates below this level are added, there is normal conversion to lactate. This determination of anaerobic glycolysis was used by both Schmid & Mahler (1959) and by Mommaerts et al. (1959) in establishing the deficiency of phosphorylase in their cases, and it clearly can be used to pinpoint the particular enzyme system requiring more specific investigation.

In most cases the muscle glycogen is raised, commonly to levels of the order of 3 to 5 g./100 g. tissue. This is about half the levels encountered in Type II glycogenosis and is presumably due to the fact that a-1, 4-glucosidase is present in normal amounts. The glycogen has been shown to have a normal structure.

Shortening of muscle on exercise, especially if it is ischaemic, is a characteristic feature of the condition, and it has already been mentioned that a likely cause for such contracture might be a considerable reduction in ATP and/or in creatine phosphate, on the analogy of the contracture occurring in rigor mortis. However, Rowland, Araki & Carmel (1965) have shown in two patients that the levels of ATP, ADP and AMP remained normal during a contracture induced by ischaemic exercise. In one patient the creatine phosphate remained unchanged though in the other there was a 50% fall in the contractured muscle, but even so the level was still within their normal range. The biochemical cause of the contracture therefore still remains unsolved.

Pathological Findings

Although the fundamental pathological feature usually seen by light microscopy is a generalized increased staining for glycogen, the most characteristic abnormality is the presence of subsarcolemmal blebs containing masses of glycogen (Schmid & Mahler, 1959). Where special precautions have not been taken to preserve the glycogen, as by fixing in Rossman's fluid, the latter will have been largely washed out and the blebs will appear as subsarcolemmal vacuoles. An occasional fibre may show hyaline necrosis or other signs of muscle damage, especially perhaps in those cases associated with myoglobinuria or myopathy, and possibly depending on whether the muscle has been recently subjected to unusual exercise. Histochemically all the muscle fibres are devoid of phosphorylase (Pearson *et al.,* 1961) whereas any arterioles that may be present show normal staining.

Schotland, Spiro, Rowland & Carmel (1965) made an electron micro-scopic study of muscle both in the resting state and at 3 and 30 mins. after sufficient ischaemic exercise to induce some contracture in muscle—the flexor carpi radialis—from two patients with proved phosphorylase deficiency. They also removed control specimens from a healthy adult under precisely the same conditions. These control biopsies showed none of the changes seen in the patients. Most of the glycogen was deposited either under the sarcolemma as in the blebs seen with light microscopy or in the intermyofibrillar space at the level of the I band. In addition there were many more glycogen granules between the thin filaments. As a result, many myofibrils appeared to be compressed or replaced by glycogen deposits. Dr. Weller has largely confirmed these findings in our recent case (Gruener, McArdle, Ryman & Weller, 1968) though the I bands were not compressed or distorted as much as in the cases of Schotland *et al.,* (1965) and there was greater separation of the myofibrils by glycogen in the region of the A bands.

Schotland *et al.* (1965) raise the possibility that this compression, displacement and possibly loss of thin filaments may be responsible for some of the permanent weakness observed in later life in some of these cases. This would seem rather doubtful and it is relevant that the triceps muscle from our recent case which was rather weak and wasted relative to the powerful leg muscles, had less glycogen, both chemically and micro-scopically, than the sartorius muscle. It would seem more likely that this weakness and wasting is due to muscle damage sustained during over-exertion. There is no doubt that this occurs in this patient especially in his upper arms which become swollen and tender after exercise and may remain sore and rather weak for a few days after. It has been noteworthy moreover that during an eight month period of follow-up that over-exertion of the upper arms rather than the legs has been followed by unusually high serum creatine phosphokinase levels (up to 2,000 IU/l). What the nature of the chemical change directly responsible for the muscle damage (inadequate substrate ?, the shift to an alkaline pH?) and why this should be manifested largely if not entirely in the upper arms or at any rate above the pelvis is entirely speculative.

Schotland *et al.* (1965) found the mitochondria in the resting muscle were normal, but in the specimens removed 3 mins. after the ischaemic exercise, some of the mitochondria appeared to contain fewer cristae, and in those removed at 30 mins. some mitochondria contained vacuoles, myelin forms or collections of what appeared to be glycogen granules. In addition there were a number of lipid vacuoles adjacent to the mitochondria. The authors were careful to point out that such changes should be interpreted with caution. In what is, so far, a very preliminary study, we have been unable to find any of these changes in muscle that immediately before biopsy had been electrically stimulated to produce a contracture other than the fairly frequent occurrence of lipid vacuoles, though I doubt if these were more frequent than in the resting muscle. On the other hand in the stimulated muscle there were a number of elongated mitochondria in the larger glycogen filled spaces separating the myofilaments. Perhaps it is possible that these may represent mitochondria squeezed and dislocated from their original positions by the vigorous muscular contractions caused by the electrical stimulation and the ensuing contracture into the wider, glycogen containing, sarcoplasmic spaces between certain of the myofibrils.

Schotland *et al.* (1965) were able to find however one or two fibres in contracture—something we have not as yet been able to do. The sarcomeres were markedly shortened, the I bands were absent, the Z lines were thickened due to contraction bands and the mitochondrial changes were more frequent. Subsequent study (Gruener *et al.*, 1968) has shown that rather similar changes were seen in the immediate vicinity of those fibres of the sartorius as were in contracture and in the (resting) triceps. The presence of considerable amounts of glycogen within some of the mitochondria was particularly striking. In this region, moreover, there was prominent dilatation of the lateral vesicles of the triad, with slight dilatation of the other parts of the sarcoplasmic reticulum, the transverse tubular system remaining unaffected. In all other areas examined the sarcoplasmic reticulum was entirely normal. These latter changes are of considerable interest in relation to the genesis of the contracture that is such a characteristic feature of the syndrome. It is from the lateral vesicles of the triad that Ca.$^{2+}$ is released and reabsorbed as the result of electrical spread of the impulse along the transverse tubule, and it is this release of Ca.$^{2+}$ that initiates the contractile response of the myofibrils and its rebinding that causes relaxation. Some observations in relation to the genesis of the contracture made with Dr. Gruener will be referred to later.

Pathophysiology

Discovery of an enzyme deficiency as the ultimate cause of a disease in many ways increases rather than lessens interest in the condition, for it provides a firm basis from which the various symptoms and signs can be studied. This is especially the case with disorders of anaerobic glycolysis since the pathway blocked is important, the resulting disorders of function of considerable interest and we have not, as yet, any adequate treatment.

Exercise in these patients causes pain, disproportionate cardiovascular and respiratory embarassment and stiffness and easy fatigue of the muscles.

Muscle Pain

The pain is similar to or identical with ischaemic pain, but its cause is unknown. It would seem to be due to anoxia for, although there is a very moderate increase in oxygen consumption, there is a very greatly increased blood flow to the exercising muscles (McArdle, 1951). This hyperaemia is of interest to the physiologist since it occurs without decrease in blood pH, increase in pCO_2 or increase in blood lactate during exercise (Barcroft, Greenwood, McArdle, McSwiney, Semple, Whelan & Youlten, 1967).

Cardiovascular and Respiratory Function

Porte, Crawford, Jennings, Aber & McElroy (1966) have recently studied the cardiovascular and respiratory responses to exercise in a patient with proven phosphorylase deficiency. During exercise there was a disproportionate increase in pulse rate, a considerable rise in blood pressure, increased pressure in the right atrium and abnormal differences in arterio-venous oxygen content. Whilst they believe that an insufficient supply of substrate to the skeletal muscles is the important factor in causing the cardiac embarrassment, they also raise the possibility that the cardiac muscle may itself be involved. It may be relevant that electrocardiographic abnormalities including increased QRS voltage, T wave inversion and prolongation of the PR interval have been reported in a 19 year old youth with muscle phosphorylase deficiency (Ratinov, Baker & Swaiman, 1965). The abnormalities were observed whilst at rest, but unfortunately the effect of exercise was not determined.

Porte et al. (1966) were particularly interested in the phenomenon of 'second wind' in these patients. This was induced, not only by carbohydrate infusion, but by heparin injection, noradrenaline infusion and by preliminary 'warming up'. They showed that these procedures raised the level of the plasma free fatty acids and that 'second wind' was associated with a low respiratory quotient. They suggested therefore that mobilisation of endogenous free fatty acids may provide sufficient substrate to account for 'second wind'.

Artificially raising the free fatty acids may be used as a form of treatment, and Dr. R. Mahler and I, for the last two years, have given isoprenaline to my original patient with some, though of course short lasting, improvement in exercise tolerance. My second patient has also noted improvement from isoprenaline and Saventrin (isoprenaline in a slowly released form) but unfortunately, the severity of the associated side effects outweighed the benefits, and treatment was discontinued.

Muscle stiffness and contracture

One of the most intriguing of the manifestations of the condition is the progressive muscle stiffness on vigorous exercise. It seemed worthwhile to investigate this symptom since, apart from its intrinsic interest, its prevention might constitute an alternative form of treatment to our rather ineffectual efforts to by-pass the block by raising the plasma levels of sugars and free fatty acids.

The sensation of stiffness would seem to be the expression of the gradual failure of increasing numbers of the muscle fibres to relax. This leads to progressive shortening of the muscle or muscle group as a whole, though experimentally it was possible to produced localized shortening of a portion of a muscle by exercise with this particular portion rendered ischaemic either by a plethysmographic cuff or a steel bar (McArdle, 1951). Gross shortening of muscle produced by ischaemic exercise was found by Drs. Dawson and Merton to be electromyographically silent. This finding has been confirmed by Rowland et al. (1966) and by Dyken, Smith & Peake (1967). Indeed the latter suggest that the rapid decrement in the evoked potential on supramaximal nerve stimulation in association with shortening of the muscle could be used as a rapid screening test for phosphorylase or phosphofructokinase deficiency.

The electrical silence of the shortened muscle indicates that it is in a state of physiological contracture, a situation difficult to investigate *in situ*, but one which, in biopsied muscle, it might be possible to investigate by the Natori technique. This is the elegant technique used by Costantin & Podolski (1965) to demonstrate the effect of Ca.$^{2+}$ in causing the contractile response in muscle fibres stripped of their sarcolemma by microdissection. On consulting Professor A. F. Huxley, I was lucky to be put in touch with Dr. R. Gruener who was then working with the Natori technique in Professor Huxley's laboratory.

We first showed (Gruener, McArdle, Ryman & Weller, 1968) that biopsied human muscle behaved like normal frog and rat muscle even after transport from Guy's Hospital to University College. Then, when the patient came to biopsy, a piece of sartorius was removed both before and after electrical stimulation sufficient to produce a noticeable shortening of muscle persisting after the stimulation had ceased. It was hoped to produce a state of contracture in the muscle and the appearance after stimulation was certainly compatible with this. Dr. Gruener stripped the sarcolemma from a number of fibres and made repeated focal applications of either Ca.$^{2+}$ or of caffeine with ciné recording of the responses. These were compared with the responses of normal unstimulated human muscle and of mouse muscle that had had electrical stimulation similar to that given to muscle of the patient. The responses were then compared, conclusions being verified by measurement of sarcomere length.

In the normal human fibres both Ca.$^{2+}$ and caffeine elicited contractures lasting approximately one to three seconds which were completely reversible. Moreover, exactly the same responses were obtained after many repeated focal applications. In the phosphorylase deficient muscles however, repeated application led to contractures which persisted for up to one minute. Such residual contractures occurred most readily—sometimes after the second focal application—in fibres from the muscle that had been electrically stimulated *in vivo*. The unstimulated muscle fibres showed such contractures only after five or more focal applications. No residual contractures were seen in the mouse fibres that previously had been electrically stimulated, even after repeated applications of Ca.$^{2+}$ or caffeine, nor did they differ in any way from unstimulated normal fibres.

A few of the fibres from the stimulated phosphorylase deficient muscle were still in a state of contracture. These were locally superfused with a relaxing medium containing EGTA, ATP, MgCl$_2$ histidine hydrochloride and KCl. The fibres were shown to have relaxed by measuring the sarcomere spacings before and after application of the medium.

The abnormal persistence of the contractures produced both by Ca.$^{2+}$ and by caffeine which is thought to act by antagonizing the Ca.$^{2+}$ pumping action of the sarcoplasmic reticulum (Herz & Weber, 1965; Gruener, 1967), would suggest that the Ca.$^{2+}$ binding capacity of the sarcoplasmic reticulum might be readily affected in phosphorylase deficient muscles. This would seem to be especially the case if it is accepted, as shown by Rowland *et al.* (1965) in two patients under rather similar circumstances, that the ATP content of both the resting and stimulated muscles are likely to have been normal at the time of biopsy, since a Ca.$^{2+}$ chelating system (admittedly containing ATP) relaxed contractured muscle fibres.

The position however is more complicated than I may perhaps have made it appear, in what is necessarily a very brief discussion of the results. The exact mechanism of the contracture is still uncertain and clearly requires further elucidation.

REFERENCES

ANDERSEN, D. H. (1956). *Lab. Invest.* **5**, 11.
BARCROFT, H., GREENWOOD, B., MCARDLE, B., MCSWINEY, R. R., SEMPLE, S. J. G., WHELAN, R. F., & YOULTEN, L. J. F. (1967). *J. Physiol., Lond.* **189**, 44P.
BETHLEM, J., VAN GOOL, J., HÜLSMANN, W. C., & MEIJER, A. E. F. H. (1966). *Brain* **89**, 569.
COSTANTIN, L. L. & PODOLSKY, R. J. (1965). *Fedn Proc. Fedn Am. Socs exp. Biol.* **24**, 1141.
CORI, G. T. (1957). *Mod. Probl. Paediat.* **3**, 344.
DI SANT'AGNESE, P. A., ANDERSEN, D. H., & METCALF, K. M. (1962). *J. Pediat.* **61**, 438.
DYKEN, M. L., SMITH, D. M., & PEAKE, R. L. (1967). *Neurology, Minneap.* **17**, 45.
ENGEL, W. K., EYERMAN, E. L., & WILLIAMS, H. E. (1963). *New Engl. J. Med.* **268**, 135.
FORBES, G. B. (1953). *J. Pediat.* **42**, 645.
GRUENER, R. (1967). *J. Physiol., Lond.* **191**, 106P.
GRUENER, R., MCARDLE, B. RYMAN, B. E., & WELLER, R. O. (1968). *J. Neurol. Neurosurg. Psychiat.* **31**, 268.
HATCHER, M. H., Jr., SIDBURY, J. B., Jr., & HEYMAN, A. (1964). *Neurology, Minneap.* **14**, 255.
HERZ, R. & WEBER, A. (1965). *Fedn Proc. Fedn Am. Socs exp. Biol.* **24**, 208.
ILLINGWORTH, B., CORI, G. T., & CORI, C. F. (1956). *J. biol. Chem.* **218**, 123.
LAYZER, R. B., ROWLAND, L. P., & RANNEY, H. M. (1967). *Arch. Neurol.* (*Chic*). **17**, 512.
LYON, J. B. & PORTER, J. (1963). *J. biol. Chem.* **238**, 1.
MCARDLE, B. (1951). *Clin. Sci.* **10**, 13.
MOMMAERTS, W. F. H. M., ILLINGWORTH, B., PEARSON, C. M., GUILLORY, R. J., & SERAYDARIAN, K. (1959). *Proc. nat. Acad. Sci. U.S.A.* **45**, 791.
OLINER, L., SCHULMAN, M., & LARNER, J. (1961). *Clin. Res.* **9**, 243.
PEARSON, C. M., RIMER, D. G., & MOMMAERTS, W. F. H. M. (1961). *Am. J. Med.* **30**, 502.
PORTE, D., CRAWFORD, D. W., JENNINGS, D. B., ABER, C., & MCILROY, M. B. (1966). *New Engl. J. Med.* **275**, 406.
RATINOV, G., BAKER, W. P., & SWAIMAN, K. F. (1965). *Ann. intern. Med.* **62**, 328.
ROWLAND, L. P., ARAKI, S., & CARMEL, P. (1965). *Arch. Neurol., Chicago,* **13**, 541.
ROWLAND, L. P., LOVELACE, R. E., SCHOTLAND, D. L., ARAKI, S., & CARMEL, P. (1966). *Neurology, Minneap.* **16**, 93.
SATOYOSHI, E. & KOWA, H. (1965). *Trans. Am. neurol. Ass.* **90**, 46.
SCHMID, R. & MAHLER, R. (1959). *J. clin. Invest.* **38**, 2044.
SCHOTLAND, D. L., SPIRO, D., ROWLAND, L. P., & CARMEL, P. (1965). *J. Neuropath. exp. Neurol.* **24**, 629.
SHY, G. M., GONATAS, N. K., & PEREZ, M. (1966). *Brain,* **89**, 133.
SIDBURY, J. B., GITZELMANN, R., & FISHER, J. (1961). *Helv. Paediat. Acta,* **16**, 505.
SIDBURY, J. B., MASON, J., BURNS, W. B., & RUEBNER, B. H. (1962). *Bull. Johns Hopkins Hosp.* **111**, 157.
TARUI, S., OKUNO, G., OKURA, Y., TANAKA, T., SUDA, M., & NISHIKAWA, M. (1965). *Biochem. biophys. Res. Comm.* **19**, 517.
THOMSON, W. H. S., MACLAURIN, J. C., & PRINEAS, J. W. (1963). *J. Neurol. Neurosurg. Psychiat.* **26**, 60.
WILLIAMS, H. E., KENDIG, E. M., & FIELD, J. B. (1963). *J. clin. Invest.* **42**, 656.

TYPE II (POMPE'S) SKELETAL MUSCLE GLYCOGENOSIS

P. Hudgson

ALTHOUGH skeletal muscle is involved in several of the forms of glycogen storage disease, the illness rarely presents as a myopathy. In a few such cases however the underlying metabolic defect has been elucidated and is due to deficiencies of a variety of glycolytic enzymes including muscle phosphorylase (Engel *et al.,* 1963), acid maltase (Courtecuisse *et al.,* 1965; Zellweger *et al.,* 1965; Smith *et al.,* 1966 and Isch *et al.,* 1966), amylo-1, 6-glucosidase (Oliner *et al.,* 1961) and possibly phosphoglucomutase (Thomson *et al.,* 1963). In this communication we report two cases of skeletal muscle glycogenosis with clinical features superficially resembling those of progressive muscular dystrophy and in both of whom acid maltase was deficient in skeletal muscle.

CASE HISTORIES

Case 1. This female Portuguese undergraduate aged 19, admitted to Newcastle General Hospital in August 1966, was born of unrelated parents neither of whom had any history of muscular disease in previous generations. However, an elder brother had died aged four years with pneumonia after being weak and 'floppy' from birth. No other details of his medical history are available. The patient's early development was apparently normal and she first walked at 15 months although she never learned to run well. Her gait did not become definitely abnormal until the age of 7 when she developed a transient right hemiplegia after a minor febrile illness. The hemiplegia cleared completely but from this time onwards her gait became increasingly abnormal and her arms weak. These symptoms progressed slowly but steadily and became very much worse during inter-current illnesses. Recovery of strength was incomplete after these episodes. A few months before admission to hospital in Newcastle she had the first of a series of attacks of dysphagia and she had recently complained of slight dyspnoea on exertion. There was no history of muscle cramps or stiffness at any stage during the illness.

On examination she was of normal general appearance although of rather short stature (150 cm.). She had a dorsal and lumbar scoliosis with accentuation of the lumbar lordosis. Her gait was slow and waddling, she had great difficulty in climbing stairs and she was unable to run or rise from a low chair. Examination of the cardiovascular system revealed only a soft short mid-systolic bruit over the pulmonary area. Electrocardiograms (E.C.G.'s) done before and after effort were normal. There was generalized hypotonia, weakness and wasting of the skeletal muscles, the last being less pronounced than expected in view of the widespread weakness. The para-spinal muscles, the flexors and extensors of the hips and the thigh muscles were particularly severely affected. Neurological examination revealed absence of the deep tendon and superficial abdominal reflexes but there was otherwise no evidence of a neurological deficit. Electromyography of the right biceps showed that there was no spontaneous activity but needle movement provoked pseudomyotonic discharges and volitional activity produced a myopathic pattern. Nerve conduction velocities in the upper and lower limbs were normal. The patient returned to Portugal in November 1967. Her condition remained essentially unaltered until January this year when she began to deteriorate and at the end of January she quite suddenly developed cardiac failure and died. Unfortunately no autopsy was obtained.

Case 2. The second patient, a 44 year old English housewife, was also first seen by us in August 1966 when a presumptive diagnosis of limb-girdle muscular dystrophy was made. Her parents were unrelated, her brother and his children and her own sons aged 13 and 10 were normal and there was no history of neuromuscular disease in previous generations. She had been normal herself until 31 when a few months after the birth of her first child she developed aching pains in both glutei and later in the lumbar muscles. Subsequently she experienced increasing difficulty in running and in climbing stairs and in carrying weights because of the weakness of her back. The latter remained her most severe disability but she had recently developed burning paraesthesiae in her tongue. She had no other symptoms of any kind. Physical examination showed that she had a moderately severe proximal myopathy particularly affecting the paraspinal muscles in the lumbar region, the hip girdles and the thighs. Apart from wasting of the sternocostal heads of the pectorals, the muscles of the shoulder girdles and upper limbs were not affected. The only other abnormal physical sign was slight enlargement of the tongue. No abnormalities were found in the cardiovascular system and the E.C.G. was normal. Electromyography of the left biceps femoris showed a myopathic pattern and needle movement provoked numerous pseudomyotonic discharges.

BIOCHEMICAL FINDINGS

Intravenous injection of adrenaline 0·4 mg. and glucagon 1·0 mg. pro-duced normal hyperglycaemic responses in each case. Blood lactate was determined before and after ischaemic exercise in each patient. In Case 2 a normal response was obtained but in Case 1 lactate concentration did not increase. A normal rise in blood lactate occurred in both patients after administration of 30 grams fructose orally.

Muscle biopsies were obtained under general anaesthesia from the biceps brachii (Case 1) and the right biceps femoris (Case 2). Control material was obtained from 6 volunteers (abdominal muscle in 4, paraspinal muscle in 1 and quadriceps in 1) and from two patients who had been treated with thiobendazole for strongyloidiasis and who had developed muscle cramps during the course of treatment. No histopathological abnormalities of any kind were found in these controls.

A portion of each biopsy was rapidly frozen in liquid nitrogen for quantitative analysis and for histochemical study (see below). The total muscle glycogen expressed as a percentage of wet weight was 5·6 per cent in Case 1 and 5·3 per cent in Case 2. Analysis of the enzymes of the glycolytic pathway showed that the activity of phosphoglucomutase, hexosephosphate isomerase, adenylate kinase and phosphorylase kinase was normal in both patients. Muscle phosphorylase activity was normal in Case 1 and just below the lower limit found in our control subjects in Case 2. The variations in maltase activity with pH were measured. In both patients the activity of this enzyme at acid pH was much lower than normal whereas neutral maltase activity was in the upper part of the normal range. Leucocyte α glucosidase activity was assayed in Case 2 only and was normal. Production of lactate by in vitro anaerobic glycolysis was normal in both patients.

Structural analysis of the muscle glycogen in Case 1 showed normal branching with no evidence of a limit dextrin structure.

PATHOLOGICAL STUDY

Eight to twelve μ sections were cut from each of the quick frozen muscle samples in a Dittes 'Cryostat' at —30° C. and were stained for succinate dehydrogenase and muscle phosphorylase activity. Half the muscle for electron microscopy (from Case 2 only) was fixed in buffered osmium tetroxide at 4° C. and half in 5 per cent glutaraldehyde followed by post-osmication in Palade's solution. Some material was stained with 5 per cent phosphotungstic acid in absolute alcohol after dehydration and both the stained and unstained muscle was embedded in 'Araldite' or in 'Vestopal'. Sections were cut at 400-500 Angstrom units (Å) with glass knives on a Porter-Blum MT/2 ultratome. The unstained sections were stained on grids with a combination of uranyl acetate and lead citrate. All the sections were examined in a modified Siemens Elmiskop I electron microscope.

For routine histological examination muscle from each biopsy was fixed in formol-calcium and in Gendre's alcoholic picric acid solution and embedded in paraffin wax. Five μ sections from the formol-calcium fixed material were fixed with haematoxylin-eosin, haematoxylin-van Gieson and phosphotungstic acid-haematoxylin (PTAH). Sections from both the formol-calcium and the Gendre fixed material were stained with alcoholic periodic acid-Schiff (P.A.S.) controlled by predigestion with diastase (salivary amylase). 'Buffy-coat' smears of the patients' peripheral venous blood were made and were stained with alcoholic P.A.S.

RESULTS

Light microscopic observations

In both cases the diagnosis of severe vacuolar myopathy, first made by examination of haematoxylin-eosin stained 'cryostat' sections, was confirmed by examination of paraffin sections (Fig. 1). In each biopsy the vast majority

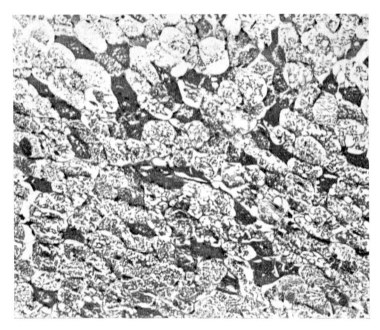

FIG. 1

Case 1. Transverse section from the Biceps biopsy showing the gross vacuolar myopathy. The larger vacuoles are situated immediately under the sarcolemma and the smaller ones are distributed randomly throughout the fibres. Haematoxylin and eosin. × 240.

of the fibres in both the longitudinal and transverse sections showed gross vacuolar change. The vacuoles showed considerable variation in size and distribution, the smaller ones being scattered uniformly throughout the fibres, the larger ones, in most cases, being situated immediately below the sarcolemma. Apart from the vacuolar change however the fibres showed remarkable little histological evidence of active degenerative change *viz.*, abnormal variation in fibre diameter, necrosis, phagocytosis and regenerative activity, interstitial fibrosis or fatty infiltration. The vacuolar change in Case 2 was perhaps a little less severe than in Case 1 but there was more histological evidence of 'myopathic' degeneration (Fig. 2).

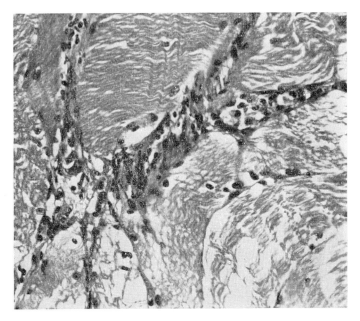

FIG. 2

Case 2. Transverse section from the Hamstring biopsy. A small
focus of necrosis and phagocytosis can be seen in the centre of the
illustration. Haematoxylin and eosin. × 308.

The basis of the vacuolar change in each biopsy was revealed by the
alcoholic P.A.S. stain. Compared with control material (from a young
adult volunteer of the same sex with epilepsy but without evidence of
myopathy), the muscle fibres contained enormously increased amounts of
P.A.S. positive material (Fig. 3) which, since it became P.A.S. negative
after predigestion with diastase (Fig. 4) was concluded to be glycogen.
The structural changes described above closely resemble those recorded in
previous reports of skeletal muscle glycogenosis (Krivit *et al.*, 1953; di
Sant' Agnese *et al.*,, 1962; Thomson *et al.*, 1963; Zellweger *et al.*, 1965;
Isch *et al.*, 1966 and Smith *et al.*, 1966).

Other histochemical studies showed that the amount and distribution of
succinate dehydrogenase activity was normal in both cases. Muscle phosphorylase activity was normal in Case 1 but appeared to be weak in Case 2
corresponding with the low activity found on quantitative assay. Examination of the 'buffy coat' smears stained with alcoholic P.A.S. appeared to
show an increase in the leucocyte glycogen in both cases compared with
control smears but examination of skin sections from Case 2 revealed no
histological abnormalities.

FIG. 3(A)

Case 2. Transverse section from the Hamstring biopsy showing the clumps and granules of P.A.S. positive material lying within the vacuoles in the muscle fibres. Alcoholic P.A.S. × 275.

FIG. 3(B)

Case 1. Longitudinal section from the Biceps biopsy showing changes similar to those illustrated in Figure 3 (a). Alcoholic P.A.S. × 275.

D

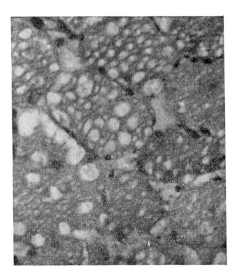

FIG. 4

Case 1. Transverse section from the Biceps biopsy.
Control confirming that the P.A.S. positive material
within the vacuoles was glycogen. Alcoholic P.A.S.
after pre-digestion with diastase. × 320.

Electron Microscopic observations

Material for electron microscopic study was available in Case 2 only.
The sections examined have shown abnormalities like those previously
described in skeletal muscle glycogenosis due to acid maltase deficiency
(Zellweger *et al.,* 1965; Courtecuisse *et al.,* 1965; Cardiff, 1966 and Isch
et al., 1966) and, more recently, in a study of muscle biopsies from a family
with McArdle's disease Salter *et al.,* (1967). Both transverse and longitudinal
sections showed large deposits of finely granular interfibrillar material
which appeared to be lying free in the sarcoplasm (Fig. 5). This material
stained intensely with uranyl acetate-lead citrate (Fig. 6) strongly suggesting
that it was glycogen.

In addition numerous vacuoles were seen in the fibres lying between the
fibrils and under the sarcolemma (Fig. 7). These were lined by a single
limiting ('unit') membrane and varied considerably in their greatest dimen-
sion from about 400 Å to several microns. Many of these contained glycogen granules (Fig. 8) and most of the smaller ones contained quite large
(approximately 200 Å in diameter) densely osmiophilic clumps (Fig. 9).
Similar structures can be seen in the electron micrographs illustrating the
papers of Courtecuisse *et al.* (1965), Zellweger *et al.* (1965) and Cardiff
(1966). The precise nature of these clumps is of course unknown but their

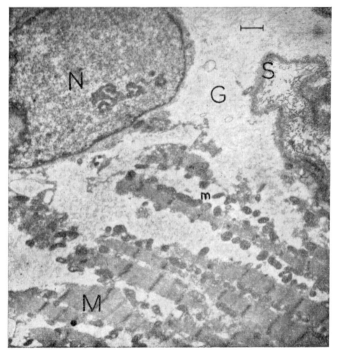

FIG. 5

Case 2. Longitudinal section from the Hamstring biopsy showing the accumulation of finely granular material between the myofibrils and under the sarcolemma. Palade, phosphotungstic acid (PTA), 'Araldite'. × 6,000.

C = collagen. G = glycogen. M = myofibril. m = mitochondria. N = nucleus. S = sarcolemma. V = vacuole. Z = Z band. The scale line on each electron micrograph is equivalent in length to 1 micron.

staining characteristics suggest that they may be composed of complex lipids, possibly glycolipids. A few much larger complex lipid figures were found lying free within the muscle fibres.

In some of the sections very large and apparently empty spaces could be seen lying immediately under the sarcolemma. These had almost certainly been filled originally with glycogen which had been washed out during the process of fixation and staining. They do not appear to be lined by membranes but they are probably derived from glycogen-filled vacuoles which have become so distended that their limiting membranes have ruptured. These spaces we believe correspond with the large subsarcolemmal spaces containing clumps of glycogen seen in the alcoholic P.A.S. stained material (Fig. 3).

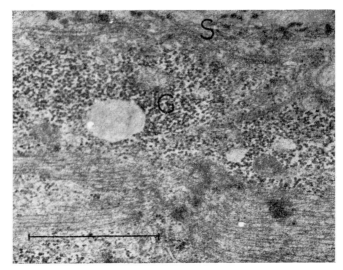

FIG. 6

Case 2. Longitudinal section from the Hamstring biopsy. Densely stained glycogen granules can be seen lying under the sarcolemma and between the myofibrils. Glutaraldehyde, Palade, 'Vestopal', uranyl acetate/lead citrate. × 36,000.

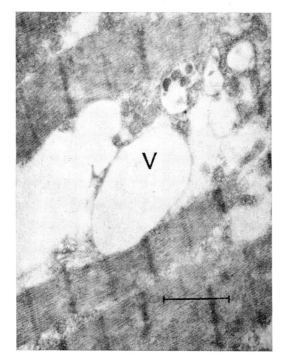

FIG. 7

Case 2. Longitudinal section from the Hamstring biopsy showing vacuoles of various sizes lying between the myofibrils. Palade, PTA, 'Araldite'. × 18,000.

The normal bilaminar structure of the sarcolemma was preserved in all of the sections examined but the sarcolemma itself was almost always invaginated. In some places this process was exaggerated giving the appearance of papillary projections arising from the surface of the muscle fibre (Fig. 10). No characteristic abnormalities have been defined in the myofibrils although they have obviously been distorted in places by the accumulations of glycogen and there were a few areas of filament fall-out. The possibility that the latter appearance was produced by minor variations in plane and

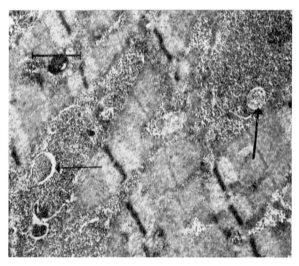

FIG. 8

Case 2. Longitudinal section from the Hamstring biopsy showing some of the vacuoles stuffed with glycogen granules. Glutaraldehyde, Palade, 'Vestopal', uranyl acetate/lead citrate.
× 13,500.

thickness of sections cannot be ruled out. However, in several areas that Z-bands showed early degenerative change of the type called 'streaming' by Rewcastle & Humphrey (1965) in their account of chloroquine myopathy in the human (Fig. 11).

The muscle nuclei were in two forms, one in which the nuclear membrane was deeply invaginated, the chromatin material aggregated in dense clumps and no nucleoli were seen, and a second in which the membrane was smooth, the chromatin finely granular and one or more nucleoli were obvious. These appearances we believe are entirely non-specific and simply represent different phases of nuclear activity, the first resting and the second where active ribonucleic acid synthesis is taking place. No

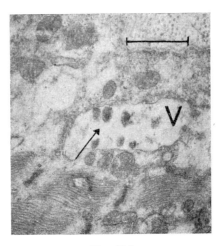

FIG. 9(A)

Case 2. Longitudinal section from the Hamstring biopsy. Medium power view of a subsarcolemmal vacuole containing a number of clumps of densely osmiophilic material Palade, PTA, 'Araldite'. × 16,800.

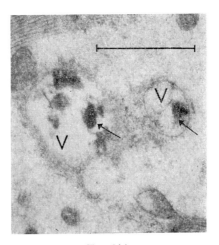

FIG. 9(B)

Higher power view of two similar vacuoles lying between myofibrils. The osmiophilic clumps are arrowed. Palade, PTA, 'Araldite'. × 26,880.

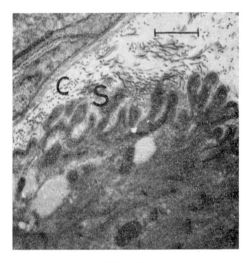

FIG. 10

Case 2. Longitudinal section from the Hamstring
biopsy showing what appear to be papillary projections arising from the sarcolemma. Palade, PTA,
'Araldite'. × 12,000.

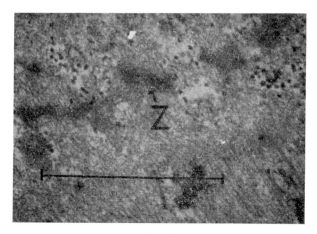

FIG. 11

Case 2. Longitudinal section from the Hamstring biopsy. The Z
bands are broadened and have lost their normal distinct outlines.
Glutaraldehyde, Palade, 'Vestopal', uranyl acetate/lead citrate.
× 51,000.

central nuclei were found and, apart from the lipid bodies previously described, there was no other electron microscopic evidence of active muscle fibre degeneration. No morphological abnormalities were found in the mitochondria or in the sacroplasmic reticulum, there was no evidence of invasion by phagocytic cells and the amount and distribution of collagen fibrils appeared to be normal.

DISCUSSION

Clinical features

Both our patients were initially diagnosed as cases of progressive muscular dystrophy. Both had slowly progressive proximal muscular weakness and neither had any other definite clinical stigmata of glycogen storage disease, nor was there any evidence of chronic denervation. In both the serum creatine kinase was increased to a level compatible with a slowly progressive muscular dystrophy and Case 1 particularly bore a close resemblance to the autosomal recessive form of juvenile dystrophy. Only the death of her brother in childhood and the unusual distribution of the muscles involved, notably relative sparing of the latissimus dorsi muscles and of the quadriceps compared with the hamstrings, suggested that this might be a different condition. The clinical features in Case 2 less closely resembled those of limb-girdle muscular dystrophy. Here the distinguishing points were the very slow progression, enlargement of the tongue and the sparing of the upper limbs, particularly the brachioradiales which tend to be involved early in limb-girdle dystrophy. In this case also the hamstrings were weaker than the quadriceps.

These clinical features obviously do not amount to a syndrome by which other cases of this condition could be recognized. On the other hand, they emphasize the diagnostic importance of the stereotyped selective patterns of muscular involvement in the muscular dystrophies.

Electromyography

In addition to evidence of myopathy, electromyography in both patients revealed abundant high-frequency discharges which did not occur spontaneously but were easily induced by needle movement or by voluntary muscle contraction. Similar discharges, usually described as 'myotonic', were described in several of the previously reported cases. We would prefer to use the term 'pseudomytonic discharges' because in our patients they differed from true myotonic discharges in two respects: the amplitude of the component potentials remained constant from beginning to end and their frequency was very nearly constant until just before the end of the discharge when it declined and then stopped abruptly. In a myotonic discharge, often after an initial increase, both the frequency and the amplitude of the component potentials gradually decay. Pseudomyotonic discharges are often found in polymyositis, occasionally in muscular dystrophy (Goodgold & Archibald, 1958 and Buchtal & Rosenfalck, 1962) and rarely in other myopathic and neurogenic disorders. In a suspected case of muscular dystrophy, however, the discovery of profuse discharges should lead to a reappraisal of the clinical findings and a confirmatory muscle biopsy.

Biochemical findings

The production of lactic acid during exercise under ischaemic conditions was measured in both cases. In Case 2 it was normal indicating normal *in vivo* muscle glycolysis. In Case 1 a flat curve was obtained but lactate production was normal after ingestion of 30 g. of fructose. These findings in Case 1 were not reflected in the *in vitro* glycolytic activity of the patient's muscle which was apparently normal. It is unfortunate that the ischaemic lactate test could not be checked in Case 1.

It was initially suspected that the discrepancy might have been due to defective *in vivo* regulation of glycolysis by a mechanism which would not be operative in a homogenate. To investigate this possibility it was considered desirable to demonstrate the presence of phosphorylase kinase activity and of adenylate kinase activity which we thought might be involved in the *control* of phosphorylase activity through production of AMP from ADP. No abnormality of these enzymes was detected. The control of glycolysis in muscle is complex and only partly understood, however, and a defect of this type could not be specifically eliminated using a homogenate from a biopsy specimen. The overall similarity of the 2 cases also argues against the involvement of this area of metabolism in the disease.

Deficiency of an acid maltase in the liver was demonstrated in a case of Pompe's disease (Type II glycogenosis) by Hers (1963). In the liver this enzyme appears normally to be located in the lysosomes and its absence might be expected to lead to accumulation of polysaccharide in the autophagic vacuoles. This localization of glycogen accumulation may explain in part the typical histological appearance in this type of glycogenosis. In skeletal muscle the existence of lysosomes has never been conclusively proved but it seems likely that they do exist and that the site of the intracellular glycogen accumulation is the same in both tissues. In muscle, as in liver, the α-glucosidase activity at acid and at neutral pH appears to be due to two different enzymes possibly with different intracellular distributions. In our patients neutral maltase activity was normal whereas the activity of the enzyme at acid pH was very much lower than normal. It is impossible, however, on these grounds alone to differentiate between an enzyme with an unusual pH optimum and an absolute enzyme deficiency.

Pathology

The key histopathological changes observed by light microscopy in the biopsies from these two patients, gross vacuolar myopathy accompanied by abnormal accumulation of glycogen within the muscle fibres, are virtually indistinguishable from those described in other reports of skeletal muscle glycogenosis (Krivit *et al.,* 1953; di Sant' Agnese *et al.,*1962; Thomson *et al.,* 1963; Zellweger *et al.,* 1965; Isch *et al.,* 1966 and Smith *et al.,* 1966). The diagnosis of a vacuolar myopathy was made in each case when the 'cryostat' sections were examined. It was obviously impossible to quantitate the amount of glycogen in muscle fibres on the basis of histochemical studies alone. However, we were able to demonstrate the presence of abnormal accumulations of glycogen in skeletal muscle in each case before quantitative analysis by comparing P.A.S. stained sections from their muscle biopsies with similar preparations from a control. In each instance the nature of the P.A.S. positive material in the muscle fibres was confirmed by staining serial sections after predigestion with diastase.

Undoubtedly the greatest interest in these cases from the morphological viewpoint lies in the changes revealed by the electron microscope. These, in addition to demonstrating vastly increased amounts of glycogen lying free in the sarcoplasm of the muscle fibres, show the presence of large numbers of vacuoles of all sizes lined by unit membranes. Many of these vacuoles contained glycogen granules (Fig. 8) but the majority of the small vacuoles contained only a small number of densely osmiophilic clumps which were much larger than the glycogen granules. These clumps were probably composed of complex lipids. Similar structures were observed in two other electron microscopic studies of skeletal muscle glycogenosis associated with acid maltase deficiency (Courtecuisse *et al.,* 1965 and Zellweger *et al.,* 1965). It may be that these structures occur only in this form of glycogen storage disease, but it is impossible to be certain about this as the accounts of electron microscopic studies in skeletal muscle glycogenosis (Courtecuisse *et al.,* 1965; Zellweger *et al.,* 1965; Cardiff, 1966 and Isch *et al.,* 1966) published to date have dealt almost exclusively with cases of acid maltase deficiency. However, it is noteworthy in this context that Salter *et al.,* (1967) found no such structures in material from 3 related cases of McArdle's disease.

The functional significance of these vacuoles is, of course, debatable but purely on morphological grounds they could reasonably be regarded as autophagic vacuoles or 'secondary' lysosomes. This concept is an attractive one as acid maltase is known to be a lysosomal enzyme in liver at least (Hers, 1963). The presence of glycogen granules and complex lipid bodies within the vacuoles is certainly consistent with the view that lysosomes maintain the integrity of the intracellular environment by 'cleaning up' debris, but the bulk of the glycogen in both cases appears to be freely dispersed in the sarcoplasm. The explanation for this is not obvious but it may be due to the rupture of overdistended vacuoles. There is no evidence in our material to support the thesis that these lysosome-like structures are derived from elements of the sarcoplasmic reticulum (Pearce, 1963 and 1966).

The relatively minor changes observed in the sarcolemma, *viz.* invagination, and formation of papillary projections (Fig. 10), appear to be a non-specific reaction to noxious stimuli of various kinds and have been seen in thyrotoxic myopathy (Engel, 1966a), McArdle's disease (Pearce, 1967), experimental chloroquine myopathy in the rabbit (Aguayo & Hudgson, 1968) and in the autosomal recessive form of juvenile muscular dystrophy (Hudgson, 1968). Their significance is unknown but they may represent an attempt by the muscle fibre to increase its surface area to deal with augmented metabolic exchange under pathological conditions. The presence of early Z-band degeneration ('streaming') (Fig. 11) is also likely to be a non-specific reaction as it has now been reported in a wide variety of spontaneously occurring and experimental myopathies (Price *et al.,* 1962; Afifi *et al.,* 1965; Rewcastle & Humphrey, 1965; Engel, 1966b; Aguayo & Hudgson, 1968; Hudgson, 1968 and Rose *et al.,* 1967) and in acutely denervated rat muscle (Pellegrino & Franzini, 1963).

Finally, it is probably highly significant that none of the gross destructive changes reported in other myopathies particularly Duchenne type progressive muscular dystrophy. murine dystrophy and polymyositis (Milhorat *et al.,* 1966; Wechsler, 1966; Hudgson, *et al.,* 1967 and Rose *et al.,* 1967) have been found in the material from these cases in spite of the fact that there had been clinical evidence of affection for 12 years and 13 years respectively. This suggests that the abnormality of the contractile mechanism in these cases may be due principally to mechanical distortion of the muscle fibre by the accumulated glycogen rather than to progressive degeneration of its ultrastructural components. If this is the case there is a very real prospect that effective treatment of the metabolic defect would result in arrest or even reversal of the morphological abnormality.

Acknowledgements

I wish to express my gratitude to Miss Hazel Caulfield and Mr. J. Fulthorpe, F.I.M.L.T. for technical assistance and to Miss Y. Riches who typed the manuscript. I would also like to thank Dr. Brian McArdle for his helpful advice on the classification of the skeletal muscle glycogenoses and Professor D. J. Manners who carried out the structural analysis of muscle glycogen in Case 1. This work was carried out with the assistance of grants from the Medical Research Council, the Muscular Dystrophy Associations of America, Inc. and the Muscular Dystrophy Group of Great Britain.

REFERENCES

AFIFI, A. K., SMITH, J. W., & ZELLWEGER, H. (1965). *Neurology (Minneap)* **15**, 371.
AGUAYO, A. J. & HUDGSON, P. (1968). In preparation.

BUCHTHAL, F. & ROSENFALCK, P. (1963). In *Muscular Dystrophy in Man and Animals,* ed. Bourne, G. H. and Golarz, M. N. Karger: Basel and New York.

CARDIFF, D. R. (1966). *Pediatrics, Springfield* **37**, 249.

COURTECUISSE, V., ROYER, P., HABIB, R., MONNIER,C., & DEMOS, J. (1965). *Archs fr. Pédiat.* **22**, 1153.

ENGEL, A. G. (1966*a*). *Mayo Clin. Proc.* **41**, 785.

ENGEL, A. G. (1966*b*). *Mayo Clin. Proc.* **41**, 713.

ENGEL, W. K., EYERMAN, E. L., & WILLIAMS, H. E. (1963). *New Engl. J. Med.* **268**, 135.

GOODGOLD, J. & ARCHIBALD, K. C. (1958). *Archs phys. Med. Rehabil.* **39**, 20.

HERS, H. G. (1963). *Biochem. J.* **86**, 11.

HUDGSON, P. (1967). In *Proceedings of the Fourth Symposium of the Muscular Dystrophy Group of Great Britain,* Pitman Medical Publications, London.

HUDGSON, P., PEARCE, G. W., & WALTON, J. N. (1967). *Brain,* **90**, 565.

ISCH, F., JUIF, J-G., SACREZ, R., & THIEBAUT, F. (1966). *Pédiatrie,* **21**, 71.

KRIVIT, K. W., POLGLASE, W. J., GUNN, F. D., & TYLER, F. H. (1953). *Pediatrics, Springfield* **12**, 165.

MILHORAT, A. T., SHAFIQ, S. A., & GOLDSTONE, L. (1966). *Ann. N.Y. Acad. Sci.* **138**, 246.

OLINER, L., SCHULMAN, M., & LARNER, J. (1961). *Clin. Res.* **9**, 243.

PEARCE, G. W. (1963). In *Muscular Dystrophy in Man and Animals,* ed. Bourne, G. H. and Golarz, M. N. Karger: Basel and New York.

PEARCE, G. W. (1966). *Ann. N.Y. Acad. Sci.* **138**, 138.

PRICE, H. M., PEASE, D. G., & PEARSON, C. M. (1962). *Lab. Invest.* **11**, 549.

REWCASTLE, N. B. & HUMPHREY, J. G. (1965). *Archs Neurol. Chicago,* **12**, 570.

ROSE, A. L., WALTON, J. N., & PEARCE, G. W. (1967). *J. Neurol. Sci.* **5**, 457.

SALTER R. H., ADAMSON, D. G., & PEARCE, G. W. (1967). *Quart. J. Med.,* **36**, 565.

DI SANT' AGNESE, P. A., ANDERSEN, D. H., & METCALF, K. M. (1962). *J. Pediat.* **61**, 438.

SMITH, H. L., AMICK, L. D., & SIDBURY, J. B. (1966). *Am. J. Dis. Child.* **111**, 475.

THOMSON, W. H. S., MACLAURIN, J. C., & PRINEAS, J. W. (1963). *J. Neurol. Neurosurg. Psychiat.* **26**, 60.

WECHSLER, W. (1966). *Ann. N.Y. Acad. Sci.* **138**, 113.

ZELLWEGER, H., BROWN, B. I., MCCORMICK, W. F., & TU, J-B. (1965). *Annls paediat.* **205**, 413.

DISCUSSION OF PRESENTATION BY
DR. McARDLE AND DR. HUDGSON

Walton (Newcastle). Has fructose a role to play in the therapy of these cases? In our experience it is not very helpful. Indeed in one patient it seemed to have the opposite effect.

Hudgson. We gave fructose to our Portuguese patient and this made her worse.

McArdle. Mahler did this and noted some improvement but in some cases abdominal symptoms developed. In general glucose, fructose and various other sugars have not been very satisfactory. Improvement is not really sufficient to justify this therapy.

From the floor. I have had two cases where there was C.N.S. involvement— mental deficiency and neurological abnormality. Would Dr. Hudgson comment on this aspect?

Hudgson. Neurological examination revealed absence of deep tendon and abdominal reflexes in Case 1 but there was no neurological abnormality in Case 2. The first patient was a brilliant Portuguese University student who spoke nine languages fluently and the other patient was of average intelligence.

Walton. Pompe's patient had C.N.S. abnormality.

Gardener-Medwin (Newcastle). What was the most striking feature of your cases, Dr. Hudgson?

Hudgson. I think the severity of the muscle involvement in both and the absence or virtual absence of liver, cardiac and C.N.S. abnormality. The Portuguese girl did, however, develop cardiac failure and C.N.S. involvement but only in the last few weeks of her life.

Walton. Five or six years ago, a boy of 13 was referred to my Department. He had lived in Rhodesia and, whilst there, had complained whilst cycling home from school that his calves had become very painful and he had had to get off his cycle and rest. He was admitted to hospital there, a muscle biopsy was done and he was reported as having phophorylase deficiency. He was given steroids. On his subsequent admission to Newcastle for investigation he had no symptoms of pain even after full exercise. On investigation we found no evidence of phosphorylase deficiency and muscle biopsy was normal. He apparently had completely recovered but there seemed no doubt about the diagnosis in Rhodesia.

McArdle. I have not seen a case like this and I cannot explain it.

TWO NEW INBORN ERRORS OF METABOLISM?

R. J. Pollitt and F. A. Jenner

We are at present studying two conditions which appear to have a metabolic basis. Coincidentally each of the two syndromes are present in a brother and his elder sister, and in each family the parents and an unaffected brother are apparently normal. In both families we were able to study the affected girls more intensely than their brothers. The chromosomes of both affected girls appeared to be normal. Thus, both these conditions are probably carried by autosomal recessive genes.

Condition characterized by AADG

The first condition is manifested chemically by the appearance of an unusual substance in the urine subjected, without preliminary treatment, to high-voltage electrophoresis at pH 2. On staining with ninhydrin-collidine-acetic acid reagent a yellow-brown spot can clearly be seen in the urines of the affected siblings, but not in those of the unaffected members of the family. The mobility of this substance is 0·37 that of glycine (correcting for electro-osmotic flow by the position of urea) and its intensity is roughly equal to that of the serine spot.

Clinically the brother and sister present different pictures, but both are severely subnormal. The girl is 31, the first child, following an unexceptional pregnancy and birth. She was soon noted to be a good, inactive, placid and backward child who could gain little from a normal education. At present she is estimated as functioning at the 2-3 year level with little potential for additional learning.

On physical examination she is large and ungainly with a vacant expression and coarse features with thick sagging facial skin. She has a dorsal scoliosis and a short neck. She has a fibrous Dupytren's like contracture of her right hand which has been slowly progressing over at least the last ten years, and she has small thumbs, but the other fingers are long and tapering.

Radiological studies show that the metacarpals and some of the phalanges are long compared to their width, but the metacarpal index is 7·7, a high but normal value. The body measurements are not consistent with the diagnosis of Marfan's syndrome. There is a systolic murmur unaccompanied by thrill, maximal at the base and conducted to the neck. Cardiac function and the electrocardiogram however appear to be normal. Extensive routine chemical pathological studies give normal results except for an apparent and unusual deficiency of cerebrospinal fluid albumin. Studies of serum glycoproteins are in progress.

The electroencephalogram shows a marked alpha variant being composed of mixtures of 6 and 12 Hertz alternating independently on the two sides.

The patient was referred to this Unit because she is reported to have a manic depressive psychosis, in which the active periods have occurred each year since she was 21 and to have lasted longer on each occasion, starting for three days in 1956 and now lasting fourteen weeks in 1967. In the inactive phase she is morose and almost completely unresponsive. In the active phase she is continually active and never sleeps. Her menarche was at 14 and her periods are normal when inactive, but irregular, scanty or absent when active.

The abnormal brother is similar in physical appearance though somewhat less retarded. Physical examination shows little of note but he has

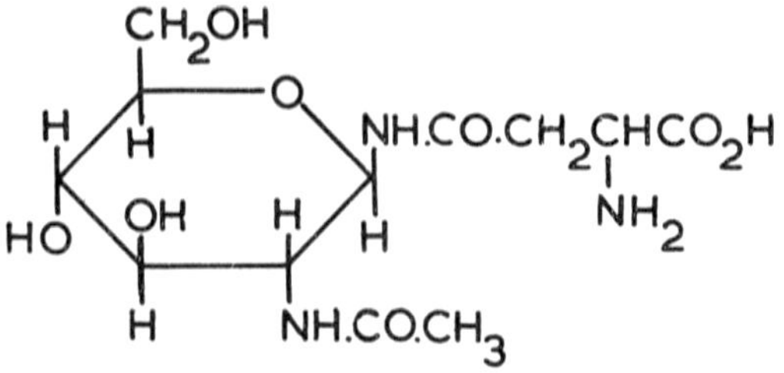

FIG. 1

2-acetamido-1-(β^1-L-aspartamido)- 1,2-dideoxy-β-D-glucose (AADG).

had petit mal like episodes starting three years ago but responding to phenytoin. His electroencephalogram is grossly abnormal with sharp waves, a spike activity followed by slow waves with clear phase reversal around the left temporal lobe. There are however independently sharp waves and slow waves in the right frontal region.

The substance in the urine of these patients responsible for the yellow spots does not appear to have been reported free in nature before. Chromatography on Sephadex G15 shows that it has a somewhat higher molecular weight than the usual urinary amino-acids. A combination of Sephadex and ion-exchange chromatography enabled us to isolate a pure sample of the compound from the urine of the girl. Its chromatographic and electrophoretic properties, hydrolysis products, infra-red spectum and elemental analysis showed that it is 2-acetamido-1-(β'-L-aspartamido)-1,2-dideoxy-β-D-glucose (AADG), Fig. 1 (Jenner & Pollitt, 1967).

AADG residues occur in nature linking carbohydrate groups to protein chains. The protein chain is continued on by peptide bonds on either side of the asparagine moiety in the usual way, while the carbohydrate chain is attached to the N-acetylglucosamine residue.

A number of other yellow-brown staining spots are seen in the patients' urine. There are three substances (and traces of others) of higher molecular weight than AADG and correspondingly lower electrophoretic mobility at pH 2. These seem to contain additional neutral carbohydrate residues—one of them gives mannose and galactose on hydrolysis. There are other high molecular weight yellow-staining compounds with very low or zero mobility at pH 2. These migrate on electrophoresis at pH 4·4 and thus contain acidic groups. Some of these compounds are converted into neutral compounds on mild hydrolysis or treatment with neuraminidase. Probably most of the acidic compounds have terminal sialic acid residues on a short carbohydrate chain.

Sometimes traces of AADG can be demonstrated in the girl's plasma. Larger quantities of AADG and traces of the other compounds seen in urine are found in the cerebrospinal fluid. After three days on a diet free of AADG or glycoprotein, there were still considerable quantities of AADG in the urine, so that at least some of the output would seem to be of endogenous origin.

The metabolic defect responsible for the presence of these compounds is still conjectural. Almost certainly the AADG comes from the breakdown of glycoproteins. Glycoprotein after digestion with a variety of proteolytic and oligosaccharide hydrolysing enzymes is reduced to AADG. This has its own hydrolysing enzyme, 2-acetamido-1-(β'-L-aspartamido)-1,2-dideoxyglucose hydrolase, which is at present not fully characterized. The enzyme has been reported in guinea-pig and hog serum, and in ram and boar epididymis. We have been looking for an easily available source in humans, as its absence in our patients could provide a basis for the chemical findings. There is not any significant activity in normal human serum or in tears or saliva. We have found, however, that human seminal fluid is very active, hydrolysing AADG to give N-acetylglucosamine and aspartic acid, but we are having some difficulty in getting seminal fluid from the subnormal brother. Nevertheless, we are still hopeful of demonstrating one way or another the presence or absence of this enzyme in our patients.

Condition characterized by brittle hair

The other condition we have been studying, in collaboration with Dr. Margaret Davies, manifests itself in defective hair. Both the children are physically and mentally retarded and have short brittle hair. Microscopically this shows trichorrhexis nodosa, a mild degree of pili torti, and an irregular surface with partial loss of the normal scale pattern. There is no argininosuccinic acid in the urine and the syndrome is clearly distinct from the sex-linked neurodegeneration described by Menkes, Alter, Steigleder, Weakly & Sung (1962).

Amino-acids in cerebrospinal fluid, plasma and urine were normal, and there were no abnormal constituents in a hydrolysate of the patient's hair. The amino-acid composition of the hair was however quite abnormal and was consistent with a considerable deficiency in the high-sulphur group of hair proteins. These proteins possibly correspond to the matrix round the keratin microfibrils and are added to the developing hair shaft within the follicle at a relatively late stage. This stage appears to be defective in our patients. It might be expected that there is an underlying metabolic error producing both the hair defect and the retardation, but so far its nature is obscure.

REFERENCES

JENNER, F. A. & POLLITT, R. J. (1967). Large quantities of 2-acetamido-1(β'-L-aspartamido)-1,2-dideoxyglucose in the urine of mentally retarded siblings. *Biochem. J.* **103**, 48-49P.

MENKES, J. H., ALTER, M., STEIGLEDER, G. K., WEAKLEY, D. R. & SUNG, J. H. (1962). A sex-linked recessive disorder with retardation of growth, peculiar hair, and focal cerebral and cerebellar degeneration. *Pediatrics, Springfield*, **29**, 764.

DISCUSSION OF PRESENTATION BY
DR. POLLITT AND DR. JENNER

Allan (Macclesfield). Brittle hair (trichorrhexis nodosa) along with mental deficiency was an outstanding feature of our cases of arginino-succin aciduria. Arginine is essential for the normal development of the feathers of the white leg-horn chicken and for the normal development of the fur of mink. Deficiency leads in the first to the frozen feathers syndrome and in the second to abnormal matted fur. We wondered if arginine deficiency might be related to the defect in the hair in our cases but were unable to confirm this. Would you comment on this?

Pollitt. The arginine content of the hair in our cases was normal.

Allan. In the case with maniac-depressive psychosis were any studies made in respect of sodium shift?

Pollitt. No studies of this nature were made because of the patient's mental condition and lack of co-operation.

NOMENCLATURE AND FUNCTION OF LIPID MOLECULES

D. N. RAINE

THE study of the complex chemistry of the fatty tissues of the body over the past 20 years has led, slowly at first but more rapidly in the last several years, to the evolution of knowledge of different species of lipids and of the greater understanding of the role these substances play in the living organism. The variety and complexity of the lipid molecules, many of which were named empirically, whether they were single species or mixtures later to be resolved, has demanded a more systematic nomenclature which is only now emerging and there is little doubt that, even now, this will require considerable extension and modification (IUPAC-IUB Commission on Biochemical Nomenclature, 1967).

However, it is helpful to consider the position at the present time as the classification of the chemical structures of these substances has accompanied and, in some instances, formed the basis for the more satisfactory classification of the disorders of lipid storage and metabolism to be described by later speakers.

It is not profitable to seek an exact definition of a lipid. Apart from being substances that are greasy to the touch, they have in common the property of being extractable from tissues by the fat solvents, ether, chloroform and benzene. This however extends the concept of a lipid to a group of smaller molecules some of which, for example cholesterol, are usefully considered with the other lipids, but other substances extracted by these solvents such as other steroids, carotenoids and some vitamins, are not intimately involved in lipid problems.

SIMPLE AND COMPLEX LIPIDS

Few would dispute the value of giving separate consideration to the simple lipids, esters of fatty acids containing between 10 and 20 carbon atoms with alcohols, the most notable of which is glycerol. These are the neutral fats and constitute the greater part of the fat of the animal body. The remainder of the lipids are complicated by the inclusion in their chemical structure of various substances such as phosphate, sugars, nitrogenous bases and derivatives of these.

The complex lipids are conveniently divided into three groups: esters of glycerol, the *glycerophosphatides**; esters of sphingosine, the *sphingolipids* and in the present state of knowledge, a miscellaneous group which includes the phosphoric esters of inositol.

* Structural formulae of several of the compounds mentioned in this paper illustrate the paper by Dr. H. Jatzkewitz later in this Symposium.

Glycerophosphatides

The glycerophosphatides include lecithin and cephalin, compounds of glycerol, phosphate and choline in the former and cholamine (ethanolamine) in the latter. Both of these names were originally applied to substances extracted from fatty tissues by certain extraction procedures and were in the first instance contaminated by a number of other substances. To distinguish the pure substances now denoted by these terms from these early preparations, the term phosphatidylcholine and phosphatidylethanolamine are commonly used. A similar substance in which serine replaces the organic base is known as phosphatidyl-serine.

Sphingolipids

The sphingolipids are derivatives of *sphingosine*, an 18 carbon compound containing two hydroxyl groups, an amino group and a double bond, which may be reduced to form an analogous series of compounds of dihydrosphingosine. One of the hydroxyl groups and the amino group are the sites at which derivatives are formed. The amino group is usually linked with a long chain fatty acid which forms an amide and, if there are no other substituents, the product is known as *ceramide*. The terminal hydroxyl group of ceramide may be linked with phosphoric acid and choline in which case the product is sphingomyelin, a substance which is present with cholesterol in greatly increased amounts in Niemann-Pick disease.

Alternatively, ceramide may be combined with a monosaccharide and thereby with sulphate, other sugars, amino sugars and similar derivatives. The latter compounds are more numerous and require further classification which is usually made on the basis of the number of hexose units attached to ceramide. The monohexosides may contain glucose or galactose and are known as *cerebrosides*. Glucocerebrosides occur in many tissues, and accumulate in the reticulo-endothelial system in Gaucher's disease. Galactocerebrosides on the other hand are largely confined to the brain. Galactocerebrosides when sulphated are known as *sulphatides* and are produced in excess in metachromatic leucodystrophy. In Krabbe's leucodystrophy, however, the formation of sulphatides appears to be impaired and there is less than the normal amount present in the brains of subjects with this disorder.

The di- and tri-hexosides consist of ceramide combined with various combinations of glucose, galactose, galactosamine and an important substance neuraminic acid, the *N*-acetyl derivative of which (NANA) is also known as sialic acid. When sialic acid is present it is attached to a galactose residue and the substances are known as *gangliosides*. The same substances without sialic acid do not have a generic name but may be referred to as glycosphingolipids or asialogangliosides. These substances are present in normal and abnormal fatty tissues and some appear to be specifically related to so-called variants of Tay-Sachs disease.

TABLE I

NOMENCLATURE OF GANGLIOSIDES

KUHN	KOREY	SVENNERHOLM	
–	G_6	G_{M3}	Ceramide-Glu-Gal(NANA)
G_0	G_5	G_{M2}	Ceramide-Glu-Gal(NANA)-Gal.NHAc (Tay-Sachs ganglioside)
G_I	G_4	G_{M1}	Ceramide-Glu-Gal(NANA)-GalNHAc-Gal
G_{II}	G_3	G_{D1a}	Ceramide-Glu-Gal(NANA)-Gal NHAc-Gal(3-NANA)
G_{III}	G_2	G_{D1b}	Ceramide-Glu-Gal(NANA)-Gal NHAc-Gal(6-NANA)
G_{IV}	G_1	G_{T1}	Ceramide-Glu-Gal(NANA)-Gal NHAc-Gal(3,6-Di NANA)

Ceramide may contain C_{18} and C_{20} sphingosines and dihydrosphingosines.

These substances together with the tetrahexosides, another important group, have been the subject of detailed study in several centres. This unfortunately has led to some confusion of nomenclature which Table I attempts to clarify. Gangliosides occur in abnormal amounts in Tay-Sachs disease and in generalized gangliosidosis, the condition in which lipid is deposited in the viscera and which has a number of features in common with Hurler's syndrome.

The nucleus of the gangliosides is the so-called Tay-Sachs ganglioside which consists of ceramide linked with glucose and then galactose to which N-acetyl neuraminic acid and N-acetyl galactosamine are combined at two separate sites. The other gangliosides are this Tay-Sachs ganglioside to which one or more groups are attached and these structures are summarized in Table I. A proportion of sphingolipids exists in the reduced form, compounds of dihydrosphingosine; but peculiar to the gangliosides is an analogous series of compounds in which sphingosine is replaced by gangliosine which resembles sphingosine closely but contains two more carbon atoms.

THE ROLE OF LIPIDS

Like many other biochemically important substances, lipids participate in active processes, for example phosphatidic acid has been invoked as a possible carrier of sodium across cellular membranes.

Much more commonly however lipids occupy a structural role and the study of the relation of this function to their structural peculiarities has been the source of a number of interesting experiments. Before considering these however it is necessary to emphasize two things. The first is that lipid molecules have a large, usually elongated or flattened structure that will not readily associate with water (hydrophobic) and a very small terminal or peripheral structure, such as an hydroxyl or a carboxyl group that has a great attraction for water. The second important point has already been hinted at in describing the hydrophobic part of the molecule, that is the actual physical shape of the lipid molecule often differs from that suggested by the chemical formula when it is written in the conventional way.

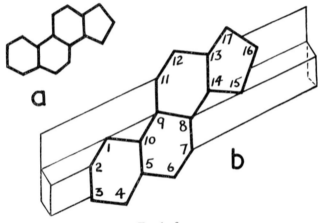

FIG. 1A & B

Steroid molecules (A) Conventional formula (B) Three dimensional structure (Shoppee, 1946).

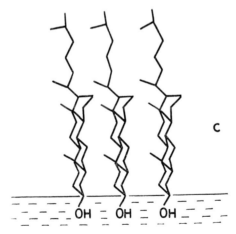

FIG. 1C

(C) Orientation of 3-hydroxysteroid molecules at an air-water interface (Willmer, 1961).

For example the steroid molecule is rather thicker in relation to its area than would be imagined from its formula (Fig. 1a, b) and a single hydroxyl group in position 3 would be sufficient to anchor the whole of the molecule to an aqueous phase (Fig. 1c). Similarly the E shaped structure implied by the usual formula for a triglyceride is very different from that revealed by x-ray diffraction studies of these substances (Fig. 2).

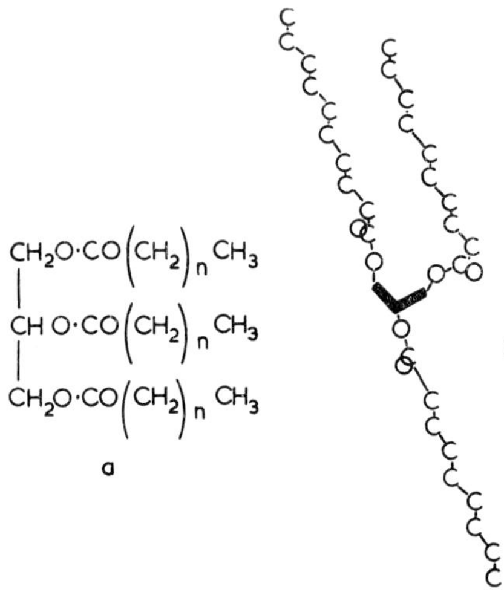

$$CH_2O \cdot CO \left(CH_2\right)_n CH_3$$
$$CH\,O \cdot CO \left(CH_2\right)_n CH_3$$
$$CH_2O \cdot CO \left(CH_2\right)_n CH_3$$

a

b

FIG. 2

Triglyceride molecule (A) Conventional formula (B) Three dimensional structure (Jensen & Mabis, 1963).

The behaviour of lipids at a water interface has been studied by means of the film balance. In this apparatus lipid molecules are spread on the surface of water in a trough so that they form an incomplete layer never more than one molecule thick. A wire is then drawn across the surface and, as it progresses, the lipid molecules are crowded together. The force necessary to move the wire can be measured and this can be related to the area into which the molecules have been compressed. From the shape of the curves that are so obtained, deductions can be made concerning the successive ways in which the molecules become packed. At first the molecules, anchored by the hydrophilic groups, lie flat on the surface of the water but finally the long hydrophobic chains or plates, as in steroid molecules, become closely packed together and project into the air, only the hydroxyl or carboxyl groups still remaining in contact with water (Fig. 3). These experiments become even more interesting when mixtures of lipids are

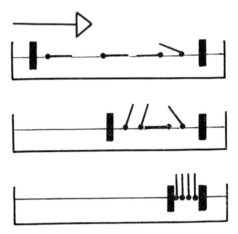

FIG. 3

Effect of progressive crowding of molecules which are largely hydrophobic but contain a small hydrophilic group.

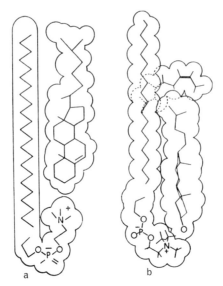

FIG. 4

Finean's model of the association of cephalin and cholesterol forming half of the lipid core of one of the two adjacent membranes which spiral to form the myelin sheath.

used and the arrangements and degrees of packing in mixtures of lecithin and cholesterol in which lecithin is present as 25, 50 and 75% of the whole are quite different (Willmer, 1961).

The structure of membranes and myelin

This question of packing becomes important in considering how biological membranes are constructed. The classical view of Danielli & Davson (1935) that the hydrophobic parts of two layers of lipid molecules form the central core of the membrane and the hydrophilic parts of the two layers of lipid form the site of attachment of protein (or mucoprotein) has received a good deal of support from recent studies. The detail however, has been refined and it seems probable that the packing of the inner core is facilitated by the presence of cholesterol and Fig. 4 shows a possible structure proposed by Dr. J. B. Finean of the University of Birmingham (who kindly provided the figure), to account for the proportions of phosphatidyl-ethanolamine (cephalin) and cholesterol in myelin.

Myelin is believed to be formed by the spiraling of an invagination of the outer membrane of a cell: thus each layer of membrane structure within the fully formed myelin sheath is, in fact, two adjacent membranes each with its bimolecular lipid structure. This can be seen in some electron micrographs and Finean's model of the structure has been modified by Vandenheuvel (1965) to fit even more closely with observations on actual myelin fragments.

REFERENCES

DANIELLI, J. F. & DAVSON, H. (1935). *J. cell. comp. Physiol.* **5**, 495.
IUPAC-IUB COMMISSION ON BIOCHEMICAL NOMENCLATURE (1967). *Biochem. J.* **105**, 897.
JENSEN, L. H. & MABIS, A. J. (1963). *Nature, Lond.,* **197**, 681.
SHOPPEE, C. W. (1946). *Rep. Prog. Chem.* **43**, 202.
VANDENHEUVEL, F. A. (1965). *Ann. N.Y. Acad. Sci.* **122**, 57.
WILMER, E. N. (1961). *Biol. Rev.* **36**, 368.

BIOCHEMICAL CLASSIFICATION OF THE SPHINGOLIPIDOSES*

D. N. RAINE

AN increasing number of diseases, some of which have been known since the nineteenth century, are undergoing a progressive subdivision into more rationally based aetiological entities. Little satisfaction seems to be achieved however until these entities can be defined in biochemical terms and it is unfortunate that, in many instances, the biochemist has taken so long to establish the criteria by which a particular diagnosis should be made that the clinician and sometimes the 'observational' pathologist have confused the situation by one or more classifications which are ultimately shown not to have any real basis. Such is the case with the group of diseases represented by the term Tay-Sachs' disease or amaurotic family idiocy.

Furthermore when the biochemist has placed a group of disorders on a rational basis, it becomes obvious that other diseases, which may be clinically quite unrelated, should logically be included in the group. Again this is illustrated by this group of neurological diseases.

EARLIER CLASSIFICATIONS

It is now clear that the sphingolipidoses are to be drawn from all of the classical groups of lipidoses, either in their entirety or, at least, from amongst the so-called variants or forme frustes. Tay-Sachs' disease has long been known to involve sphingolipid metabolism but the exact place of the 'five generally accepted variants' (Schneck, Wallace, Saifer & Volk, 1965) namely: congenital (Norman-Wood), infantile (Tay-Sachs'), late infantile (Jansky-Bielschowsky), juvenile (Spielmeyer-Vogt) and adult (Kufs) not only remained obscure but, in the last resort, has not provided a useful classification from any point of view. The variants in which the visceral organs were affected were even more difficult to account for.

In the same way Gaucher's disease has been divided into acute infantile, juvenile and chronic adult forms, the last of which is further divided into those following an autosomal recessive or dominant inheritance. Even Niemann-Pick disease, which for the most part is a disorder of sphingomyelin (not considered in the present discussion), has provided a variant which has been shown to be a sphingolipidosis of the glycolipid type. Metachromatic leucodystrophy too has been divided into infantile, late infantile, juvenile and adult forms and as yet there is no biochemical resolution of this particular disease.

* This paper, which was presented at the Sixth Annual Symposium of the Society for the Study of Inborn Errors of Metabolism, in Zurich in June 1968 was written after the present Symposium but is included with these contributions since it conveniently summarizes a section of the present work.—Eds.

A POSSIBLE SCHEME OF SPHINGOLIPID METABOLISM

Metabolic schemes often imply more than is just. When first presented they represent little more than a statement that certain chemicals have been isolated from biological sources and are now arranged in logical order based on their chemical structure. If the sequence demands a chemical that has not yet been isolated it is inserted in the scheme but enclosed in square brackets, whereupon several groups of biochemists immediately seek to demonstrate its presence in the living organism and thereby remove the brackets.

There may in addition be evidence of enzymes that can effect the step from one chemical to the next but the existence of these enzymes may only be known in different tissues or organisms. It may be a long time before the scheme is conclusively shown to exist in a given tissue and even longer before its quantitative importance is established. None-the-less such tentative statements of sequences of reaction can be useful in providing a basis for further experiment and it is in this light that the following 'metabolic chart' is presented.

These reservations are particularly important in this instance as the facts on which the scheme is based are sometimes drawn from somatic tissues and sometimes from the brain where the constituents, and hence the metabolism, are different, and furthermore they are drawn sometimes from studies of pathological material and sometimes from studies of normal tissues. The approach has been to arrange the major constituents known to accumulate in a logical order and, after filling in some gaps by implication, to seek for evidence to support the scheme as a whole. Finally, since so many recessively inherited disorders have been shown to be associated with the deficiency of an enzyme, the sites of such deficiencies that could account for a number of diseases have been indicated (Fig. 1).

EVIDENCE FOR THE EXISTENCE OF THE COMPOUNDS

The sialogangliosides

The series of compounds to the right of Fig. 1 are well established (Svennerholm, 1963); GD1a and GM1 form nearly 90 per cent of the ganglioside in normal human brain, GM2 provides a further 5 per cent and GM3 can also be detected. In contrast to brain, GM3 is the main ganglioside in parenchymatous tissues. There are in addition some gangliosides containing more than two sialic acid residues; these are not represented in Fig. 1. The precise chemical structure of GM1 has been established by Kuhn & Wiegandt (1963) as:

$$\overset{\beta}{Gal}(1 \to 3)GalNHAc\overset{\beta}{(1 \to 4)}Gal\overset{\beta}{(1 \to 4)}Glu(1 \to 1)Sphing.(2 \leftarrow)Fatty\ Acid$$
$$|$$
$$(3 \leftarrow 2)NANA$$

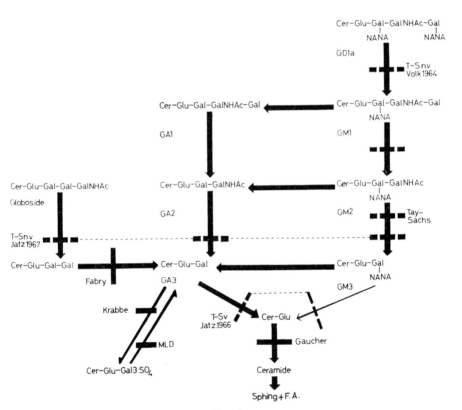

Fig. 1

Inter-relationships of some sphingolipids. The nomenclature of Svennerholm is used. T-S(n)V denotes (non)visceral variants of Tay-Sachs' disease. Where enzyme deficiencies have been demonstrated, arrows are crossed by solid bars: dotted bars represent postulated deficiencies. Unpublished evidence obtained since this figure was prepared indicates that the bar below and linking globoside, GA2 and GM2 and that below GM1 should now be solid.

In this representation the numbers in the brackets indicate the positions in the molecules nearest to them between which the link is formed and the arrow points away from the monosaccharide unit whose potential ketone (reducing) group is involved in the link. The Greek letter indicates the nature of the glycosidic link and, in all cases so far, the units are joined as β-glycosides. This is important in considering which of several related substances may be acted upon by a single enzyme.

The Tay-Sachs' ganglioside, GM2, has an exactly similar structure except that the terminal galactose is not present (Klenk, Liedtke & Gielen, 1963). Whilst the structures of the other compounds have not been elucidated with the same precision as that of GM1 and GM2 it is reasonable to suppose that the links are the same and the evidence so far available supports this.

The asialogangliosides

These compounds GA1, GA2 and GA3 (corresponding to GM1, GM2 and GM3) form the central column in Fig. 1. They have often been isolated from brains affected by pathological accumulation of the sialogangliosides but in some instances at least, they were the result of changes that had occurred during storage or extraction (Suzuki, 1965). However there are enzymes in brain which can effect the conversion of the sialogangliosides to their asialoderivatives and studies on fresh brain suggest that a proportion of the total gangliosides is normally present in this form although the extent of this and their importance has yet to be established.

The globoside series

These compounds, to the left of Fig. 1, differ from those already discussed in that the glucose and galactosamine residues are separated by two galactose units instead of one. Globoside has been obtained from normal kidney (Mårtensson, 1966) and from erythrocyte membranes (Yamakawa et al., 1963). The same substance is reported to be present in excess in the visceral organs of a patient who had many of the usual features of Tay-Sachs' disease but who was unusual in that the kidneys were histologically abnormal (Jatzkewitz, 1968).

The next compound in the series is ceramide trihexoside which occurs in traces in normal intestinal mucosa (Brady, Gal, Bradley, Mårtensson, Warshaw & Laster, 1967) and probably in most parenchymatous tissues. It has been characterised more specifically however since it is the main substance to accumulate in the visceral organs in Fabry's disease (Sweeley & Klionsky, 1963).

Further degradation in this series leads to the asialo-derivative of GM3, GA3 which has been variously known as ceramide lactoside, cytoside and cytolipin H. Because this substance has been demonstrated in both brain and visceral organs it is necessary to introduce a further distinction between the gangliosides and related compounds in the brain and in non-cerebral tissues. The difference lies in the fatty acid residue attached to sphingosine in the ceramide part of the molecule: the fatty acids in the brain gangliosides are predominantly C_{18} compounds (e.g. stearic acid) whereas those in the sphingolipids elsewhere are mainly C_{24} compounds. (e.g. lignoceric acid) (see Svennerholm, 1964). Having established this fact it is necessary to note that although GA3 is found in normal brain its fatty acids are those characteristic of the non-cerebral glycolipids (Svennerholm, 1967) suggesting that it is not an important part of the neuronal elements in the brain.

The final substance in the series is ceramide glucoside, which occurs in non-cerebral tissues normally and is the main substance to accumulate in the viscera of patients with Gaucher's disease (Philippart & Menkes, 1967). It is interesting to note however that whereas these same authors found that the brain of their subject contained an excess of galactocerebroside, the brains of patients studied by Svennerholm (1967) and by Banker *et al.* (1962) showed an excess of glucocerebroside. This may provide a biochemical basis for the subdivision of Gaucher's disease in the future.

The sulphatides

The major sulphatide is ceramide galactose 3-sulphate, the compound derived from the galactolipids. The series of compounds presently being considered all contain glucose next to the ceramide. The sulphatide corresponding to this series of compounds has been isolated by Mårtensson (1963) and shown to consist of ceramide-glucose-galactose 3-sulphate. Malone & Stoffyn (1966) too have found small amounts of this sulphatide in normal kidney and in the same organ from a case of metachromatic leucodystrophy.

EVIDENCE FOR THE EXISTENCE OF THE ENZYMES

Some of the enzymes involved in the catabolism of these compounds have been purified and studied in detail; evidence for others is derived only from studies with tissue homogenates. In a few instances there is evidence for the biosynthetic enzyme activity but in most instances it is not yet established whether this is the reverse of the catabolic reaction or whether a different enzyme is involved.

Neuraminidases

The action of these enzymes is required for the conversion of GD1a to GM1, and the three sialogangliosides GM1, GM2, and GM3 to their asialoderivatives GA1, GA2 and GA3. Such an enzyme has been demonstrated in human cerebral cortex, optimal activity being obtained at the acid pH of 3·5 (Morgan & Laurell, 1963). A more detailed study (Leibovitz & Gatt, 1968) of a calf brain, membrane bound, neuraminidase has shown that this enzyme has some degree of specificity. Whereas it would convert GD1a to GM1 it would not act on either the latter (to produce GA1) or on GM2 (to produce GA2). When the sugar residues have been removed however leaving the remaining sialic residue attached to a terminal galactose, as in GM3, the enzyme would again act to form GA3. It is not yet known whether other neuraminidases are present which will act on GM1 and GM2, for example, or whether the asialo forms of these are only formed during storage in formalin.

Galactosidases

These enzymes are required to convert (1) GM1 to GM2 and GA1 to GA2, (2) GA3 to ceramide glucoside and (3) ceramide trihexoside to GA3. In this case it is certain that more than one enzyme is involved for intestinal mucosa from a patient with Fabry's disease will effect reaction (2) but not reaction (3) (Brady, Gal, Bradley, Mårtensson, Warshaw & Laster, 1967) whereas in normal tissue reaction (3) can be demonstrated (Brady, Gal, Bradley & Mårtensson, 1967).

An enzyme from rat brain catalysing reaction (2) has been studied in detail by Gatt & Rapport (1966) and a galactosidase from rat brain which effects both parts of reaction (1) and, rather less effectively, reactions (2) and (3) has been studied by Gatt (1967).

Galactosaminidases

Enzymes with this action are required for the conversion of GM2 to GM3, GA2 to GA3 and globoside to ceramide trihexoside. A preparation from calf brain has been shown to effect all of these reactions (Frohwein & Gatt, 1967) and the authors suggest the same enzyme may be involved in all three. This is supported by the study by Jatzkewitz (1968) of a patient with the clinical features of Tay-Sachs' disease but in whom the biochemical findings were unusual in that all three substances, globoside, GA2 and GM2 accumulated. (The fact that in the usual form of Tay-Sachs' disease only GM2 accumulates to any extent does not necessarily conflict with this argument as there are other reasons why Tay-Sachs' disease may not be due simply to a deficiency of the galactosaminidase converting GM2 to GM3, *vide infra*.).

Ceramide glucosidase

Enzyme activity has been shown to be present in normal spleen homogenate and to be greatly reduced in Gaucher's disease (Patrick, 1965; Brady, *et al.*, 1965, 1966). A similar enzyme from ox brain has been studied in detail by Gatt (1966a).

Ceramidase

Finally, the enzyme separating the fatty acid residue from sphingosine in ceramide has been shown to be present in brain by Gatt (1963, 1966b).

EVIDENCE FOR THE ASSOCIATION OF DISEASE WITH ENZYME DEFICIENCIES

A number of diseases have been studied in sufficient detail to suggest that they might be associated with deficiencies in one of the enzymes involved in the metabolic reactions depicted in Fig. 1. They are discussed in the order of diminishing complexity of the major constituent involved.

Gangliosidosis GD1a

A patient with so-called late infantile amaurotic idiocy has been described by Volk, Wallace, Schneck & Saifer (1964). This non-Jewish boy whose
speech was delayed, developed progressive motor weakness from about 18
months of age until at 30 months he was ataxic. Brain biopsy showed that
the ganglion cells were balooned with lipid as is seen in the more usual
infantile form of Tay-Sachs' disease. Chromatographic examination of the
lipid however, showed that 90 per cent of it had the mobility of the normal
ganglioside GD1a although no structural studies were done on the small
amount of material available.

In the normal brain, gangliosides are present to a smaller extent than was
found in this patient and GD1a forms only half of the total. Such an
accumulation could be accounted for by a deficiency of a neuraminidase
but, as no studies of this enzyme were made, such a deficiency can only be
inferred.

Gangliosidosis GM1

Variously named generalized gangliosidosis, pseudo-Hurler disease,
Tay-Sachs' disease with visceral involvement, familial neuro-visceral
lipidosis, this is a severe progressive cerebral degeneration which usually
proves fatal in the first two years of life. Glycolipid accumulates in neurones, liver, spleen, kidney and in bone, leading to skeletal changes similar
to those of Hurler's mucopolysaccharidosis.

The lipid accumulating in the brain was shown to be GM1 the predominant fatty acid in the ceramide being C_{18}, characteristic of gangliosides of
cerebral rather than visceral origin (O'Brien, Stern, Landing, O'Brien &
Donnell, 1965). These authors did not report on lipid extracted from the
viscera but this has been studied in three patients by Suzuki (1968, see also
Suzuki, Suzuki & Chen, 1968) who found GM1 increased 20-40 fold in
both liver and spleen. Suzuki points out that this is of the same order as the
increase in another abnormal ganglioside (GM2) that occurs in the same
organs in true Tay-Sachs' disease where there is no demonstrable histological abnormality. He attributes the visceral pathology in generalised gangliosidosis to the accumulation of a mucopolysaccharide which, when
extracted, had many of the features of keratan sulphate. There do not
appear to be any enzyme studies using homogenates of tissue from patients
with GM1 gangliosidosis and so again the enzyme deficiency can only be
suspected.

GM2 Gangliosidosis (Tay-Sachs' disease)

In the typical infantile form of this disease there is progressive mental
deterioration, blindness and paralysis and, pathologically, the neurones

in the cortex of the brain are distended with accumulated lipid. Several workers have shown that this is largely GM2 (Gatt & Berman, 1963; Suzuki & Chen, 1967). At first sight this could result from a deficiency of the catabolic enzyme N-acetyl galactosaminidase. But, as will be described below under the heading of globoside gangliosidosis, a deficiency of this enzyme leads to a somewhat different disease in which globoside, GA2 and GM2 accumulate. If, then, Tay-Sachs' disease is due to a deficiency of this enzyme, it is necessary to explain why these other lipids are not found in all cases.

Doubt that this disease is due to a catabolic defect is increased by the fact that the lipids below the supposed block are slightly increased and those before the block are diminished (Svennerholm, 1967). This is exactly the reverse of what would be expected.

An alternative explanation is that there is a defect in the formation of the normal brain lipids GM1 and GD1a, which are probably formed from GM2 by the addition of galactose. Thus the deficiency may be one of galactose transferase and this has received some support from studies by Kanfer, Blacklow, Warren & Brady (1964) which suggest that GA2 is first converted to GM2 prior to the synthesis of GM1, rather than the latter being formed from its own asialo-derivative GA1. This would account for the accumulation of GM2 as it can no longer be utilized to the required extent for the synthesis of the two gangliosides which together form 90 per cent of the total ganglioside in the brain.

Gangliosidosis GM3

A non-Jewish boy suffered progressive mental and motor retardation from the age of 19 months until he died in a state of decerebrate rigidity 10 months later. The patient was not blind, there was a moderate degree of hepatomegaly but the spleen was enlarged beyond the umbilicus and the lymph nodes were generally enlarged. The histological findings, which included staining reactions before and after extraction of the tissue with solvents, were thought to be consistent with the storage of sphingomyelin and the case was regarded as one of Niemann-Pick disease (Jørgensen et al., 1964). Six years later, the tissues having meanwhile been stored in formalin, Pilz, Sandhoff & Jatzkewitz (1966) made a detailed study of the stored lipid and found GA3, GM3 and GM2 in the proportion of 10:2:3. They considered the high proportion of the asialo-derivative to be almost certainly due to the prolonged storage in formalin.

Having established the existence of this disorder it is of interest to consider whether a case reported by Maloney & Cummings (1960) might be an earlier example. This girl deteriorated mentally between the ages of 5 and 9 years. At first she required a special school but soon she developed major fits, athetoid movements and became aphasic. Her liver and spleen were never clinically enlarged. At autopsy the liver and spleen contained lipid-laden cells and lipid balooned the neurones in the brain. Chemical analysis showed the cerebroside fraction to contain both glucose and galactose a finding consistent with the stored lipid being ceramide lactose, GA3, but no detailed structural studies were made. The case was regarded as one of the rare juvenile form of Gaucher's disease. Svennerholm (1966) too has briefly reported that cases regarded as infantile Gaucher's disease showed an accumulation of GM3 and GA3 in the brain.

It is not certain whether GM3 can be converted to ceramide glucoside directly (indicated by the lighter arrow in Fig. 1) or whether sialic acid is first removed to form GA3 and this is then subjected to the action of a galactosidase. Nor does the fact that both GA3 and GM3 accumulate in this disorder help to decide this question, the answer to which must await further studies. The existence of ceramide lactose galactosidase has been established by Gatt & Rapport (1965), Hajra et al. (1966) and by Brady, Gal, Bradley & Mårtensson (1967). Using ^{14}C labelled substrate, the activity of this enzyme has been shown to be normal in a case of Fabry's disease (Brady, Gal, Bradley, Mårtensson, Warshaw & Laster, 1967). Until further evidence is available the presumed enzyme block is depicted in Fig. 1 as affecting either or both enzymes, if indeed more than one enzyme is involved.

Gaucher's disease

The condition as it is at present defined, is almost certainly of multiple aetiology. Apart from the fact that two different forms of inheritance have been described, autosomal dominant and recessive, the disease is regarded as having three clinical forms. The acute infantile form follows an autosomal recessive inheritance and apart from hepatosplenomegaly, neurological involvement is prominent, although detailed analysis of brain lipid has not revealed any notable abnormality.

The rare juvenile form of Gaucher's disease is difficult to evaluate and the only case in which chemical studies have been made (Maloney & Cummings, 1960) has already been proposed as a case of GM3 gangliosidosis.

The usual form of Gaucher's disease is, however, the chronic form which progresses slowly, well into adult life, and the major feature of which is the massive hepatosplenomegaly, the brain being largely unaffected. It is this form which occasionally shows dominant inheritance.

It may be that the recessively inherited chronic form of Gaucher's disease is an entity and the disease for which the name should be reserved. In this chronic form of the disease the lipid in the liver and spleen is ceramide glucose (e.g. Rosenberg & Chargaff,1958) which accumulates

E

because of a deficiency in ceramide glucosidase (Patrick, 1965; Brady, Kanfer & Shapiro, 1965; Brady, Kanfer, Bradley & Shapiro, 1966) and the same enzyme has been shown to be deficient in the leucocytes of patients with this disorder (Kampine et al., 1966).

Globoside gangliosidosis

Earlier in this symposium Jatzkewitz reports a non-Jewish boy who, at 6 months, developed the typical signs and changes associated with Tay-Sachs' disease, including the cherry-red spot in the macula, and who died at 25 months. At autopsy the kidneys showed marked histological changes and analysis of the lipids showed that apart from GM2 and GA2, kidney globoside was present in the viscera. A deficiency of N-acetyl galactosaminidase has been demonstrated in this case which is reported in full by Sandoff, Andreae & Jatzkewitz (1968). Because of the accumulation of the three lipids, all with terminal galactosamine residues, it is of particular interest that the enzyme obtained from calf brain by Frohwein & Gatt (1967) has been shown to act upon these same three substrates.

Fabry's disease

The most frequent alternative name for this disease is angiokeratoma corporis diffusum. It is sex linked, only males being affected, and the clinical manifestations result from deposition of ceramide trihexoside in the tissues. This leads to nodular skin eruptions on the back and thighs and deposits in the lungs lead to respiratory difficulty at a later stage. Blood vessels develop varicosities, joints may be painful and swollen, bone necroses may occur and deposits in the kidney may lead to a diabetes insipidus-like state, many patients dying in adult life in a state of uraemia.

The structure of the ceramide trihexoside was established by Sweeley & Klionsky (1963) who have also written a very full account of the disease (Sweeley & Klionsky, 1966). The enzyme which might be presumed to hydrolyse this trihexoside has been studied in biopsies of intestinal mucosa by Brady, Gal, Bradley, Mårtensson, Warshaw & Laster (1967). In normal subjects about 6 units of activity were found whereas in two affected males there was no detectable activity. A heterozygous female was found to show an intermediate activity.

Krabbe's globoid leucodystrophy

This condition, affecting infants in the first few months of life, results in widespread degeneration of the white matter in the brain, giving rise to spastic paralysis and blindness, the patients usually dying before their third year. Peripheral nerves, too, show defective myelination (Lake, 1968). Several authors have shown that the concentration of neutral ceramide hexosides is increased, whereas the sulphated form of the same compounds is markedly deficient (Austin, 1963). Sulphatides are formed from neutral glycolipids by the action of 'active sulphate', 3'-phosphoadenosine 5'-phosphosulphate and the enzyme cerebroside sulphotransferase. The activity of this enzyme has been shown to be either very low or absent in the kidney and in both cerebral cortex and white matter in two patients with Krabbe's leucodystrophy (Bachhawat, Austin & Armstrong, 1967; Austin *et al.*, 1968).

Metachromatic leucodystrophy

This familial disorder is most common in childhood but cases have been described in adults and a few appear to have occurred from birth. Broadly speaking the duration of the illness increases with the age at which it is first recognized. Pathologically there is diffuse degeneration of myelin in the brain, associated with the accumulation in the brain and visceral organs of a lipid which shows brown metachromatic staining under certain prescribed conditions (see Bargeton, 1963).

Jatzkewitz (1968) has described vividly the way in which knowledge of this disorder has emerged, largely at his hand, and it is now established that the metachromatic lipid is an abnormal accumulation of sulphatide and that this is due to a deficiency of cerebroside sulphatase (Mehl & Jatzkewitz, 1965) a complex enzyme system which includes aryl sulphatase A. This last enzyme can be used in diagnosis as its activity in urine is unusually low in patients with this disorder (Austin, Armstrong, Shearer & McAfee, 1966).

THE BIOCHEMICAL BASIS OF VISCERAL INVOLVEMENT

The most striking example of a lipidosis, primarily affecting the brain but in which the other organs and skeleton are seriously affected is GM1 gangliosidosis, formerly known as pseudo-Hurler disease. In addition to this, however, similar, though less marked involvement of non-cerebral organs is a feature of the variant of Tay-Sachs' disease here described as GM3 gangliosidosis and also of Fabry's disease. Visceral involvement is not marked in GD1a gangliosidosis, GM2 gangliosidosis (Tay-Sachs' disease) or globoside gangliosidosis.

Suzuki (1968) has shown that the accumulation of GM2 ganglioside in the viscera in Tay-Sachs' disease (which does not show visceral involvement) is of the same order as the increase of GM1 ganglioside in the viscera in GM1 gangliosidosis and he argues that the visceral involvement in the latter cannot therefore be accounted for by the accumulation of lipid.

Examination of Fig. 1 however shows that in the disorders where the viscera are involved, a lipid with a terminal galactose residue accumulates and it might be postulated that there might be a galactosidase deficiency.

Suzuki (1968) has extracted from the organs of a patient with GM1 ganglio-sidosis a mucopolysaccharide with the properties of keratan sulphate and it becomes of special interest that, of all the mucopolysaccharides associated with the varieties of gargoylism, dermatan sulphate, heparan sulphate and keratan sulphate, the latter is the only one to contain galactose. It may well be that a common enzyme is involved in the catabolism of this mucopoly-saccharide and the gangliosides with terminal galactose residues, and it will be of interest to see if the organs of patients with Fabry's disease and GM3 gangliosidosis can be shown to contain keratan sulphate.

REFERENCES

AUSTIN, J. H. (1963). *J. Neurochem.* **10**, 921.
AUSTIN, J., ARMSTRONG, D., SHEARER, L., & MCAFEE, D. (1966). *Archs Neurol., Chicago*, **14**, 259.
AUSTIN, J., BACCHAWAT, B. K., ARMSTRONG, D., STUMPF, D., KRETSHMER, L., MITCHELL, C., & VAN ZEE, B. (1968). *J. Neuropath. exp. Neurol.* **27**, 141.
BACHHAWAT, B. K., AUSTIN, J., & ARMSTRONG, D. (1967). *Biochem. J.* **104**, 15C.
BANKER, B. Q., MILLER, J. Q., & CROCKER, A. C. (1962). In *Cerebral Sphingo-lipidoses* p. 73. Ed. Aronson, S. M. and Volk, B. W. New York: Academic Press.
BARGETON, E. (1963). In *Brain lipids and lipoproteins and the leucodystrophies* p. 90. Ed. Folch-Pi, J. and Bauer, H. J. Amsterdam: Elsevier.
BRADY, R. O., GAL, A. E., BRADLEY, R. M., & MÅRTENSSON, E. (1967). *J. biol. Chem.* **242**, 1021.
BRADY, R. O., GAL, A. E., BRADLEY, R. M., MÅRTENSSON, E., WARSHAW, A. L., & LASTER, L. (1967). *New Engl. J. Med.* **276**, 1163.
BRADY, R. O., KANFER, J. N., BRADLEY, R. M., & SHAPIRO, D. (1966). *J. clin. Invest.* **45**, 1112.
BRADY, R. O., KANFER, J. N., & SHAPIRO, D. (1965). *Biochem. Biophys. Res. Commun.* **18**, 221.
FROHWEIN, Z. & GATT, S. (1967). *Biochemistry, N.Y.* **6**, 2783.
GATT, S. (1963). *J. biol. Chem.* **238**, 3131.
GATT, S. (1966a). *Biochem. J.* **101**, 687.
GATT, S. (1966b). *J. biol. Chem.* **241**, 3724.
GATT, S. (1967). *Biochim. biophys. Acta*, **137**, 192.
GATT, S. & BERMAN, E. R. (1963). *J. Neurochem.* **10**, 43.
GATT, S. & RAPPORT, M. M. (1965). *Israel J. med. Sci.* **1**, 624.
GATT, S. & RAPPORT, M. M. (1966). *Biochem. J.* **101**, 680.
HAJRA, A. K., BOWEN, D. M., KISHIMOTO, Y., & RADIN, N. S. (1966). *J. Lipid Res.* **7**, 379.
JATZKEWITZ, H. (1968). This symposium.
JØRGENSEN, L., BLACKSTAD, T. W., HARKMARK, W., & STEEN, J. A. (1964). *Acta Neuropath.* **4**, 90.
KAMPINE, J. P., BRADY, R. O., KANFER, J. N., FELD, M., & SHAPIRO, D. (1966) *Science, N.Y.* **155**, 86.
KANFER, J. N., BLACKLOW, R. S., WARREN, L., & BRADY, R. O. (1964). *Biochem. biophys. Res. Commun.* **14**, 287.
KLENK, E., LIEDTKE, U., & GIELEN, W. (1963). *Hoppe-Seyler's Z. physiol. Chem.* **334**, 186.
KUHN, R. & WIEGANDT, H. (1963). *Chem. Ber.* **96**, 866.
LAKE, B. D. (1968). *Nature, Lond.* **217**, 171.
LEIBOVITZ, Z. & GATT, S. (1968). *Biochim. biophys. Acta*, **152**, 136.
MALONE, M. J. & STOFFYN, P. (1966). *J. Neurochem.* **13**, 1037.
MALONEY, A. F. J. & CUMINGS, J. N. (1960). *J. Neurol. Neurosurg. Psychiat.* **23**, 207.

MÅRTENSSON, E. (1963). *Acta chem. scand.* **17**, 1174.
MÅRTENSSON, E. (1966). *Biochim. biophys. Acta,* **116**, 296.
MEHL, E. & JATZKEWITZ, H. (1965). *Biochem. biophys. Res. Commun.* **19**, 407.
MORGAN, E. H. & LAURELL, C. B. (1963). *Nature, Lond.* **197**, 921.
O'BRIEN, J. S., STERN, M. B., LANDING, B. H., O'BRIEN, J. K., & DONNELL,
  G. N. (1965). *Am. J. Dis. Child.* **109**, 338.
PATRICK, A. D. (1965). *Biochem. J.* **97**, 17C.
PHILIPPART, M. & MENKES, J. H. (1967). In *Inborn Disorders of Sphingolipid
  Metabolism* p. 389. Ed. Aronson, S. M. and Volk, B. W. Oxford: Pergamon.
PILS, H), SANDHOFF, K. & JATZKEWITZ, H. (1966). *J. Neurochem.* **13**, 1273.
ROSENBERG, A. & CHARGAFF, E. (1958). *J. biol. Chem.* **233**, 1323.
SANDHOFF, K., ANDREAE, V., & JATZKEWITZ, H. (1968). *Life Sciences,* **7**, 283.
SCHNECK, L., WALLACE, B. J., SAIFER, A., & VOLK, B. (1965). *Am. J. Med.* **39**,
  285.
SUZUKI, K. (1965). *J. Neurochem.* **12**, 629.
SUZUKI, K. (1968). *Science, N.Y.* **159**, 1471.
SUZUKI, K. & CHEN, G. C. (1967). *J. Lipid Res.* **8**, 105.
SUZUKI, K., SUZUKI, K., & CHEN, G. C. (1968). *J. Neuropath. exp. Neurol.* **27**,
  15.
SVENNERHOLM, L. (1963). *J. Neurochem.* **10**, 613.
SVENNERHOLM, L. (1964). *J. Lipid Res.* **5**, 145.
SVENNERHOLM, L. (1966). *Biochem. J.* **98**, 20P.
SVENNERHOLM, L. (1967). In *Inborn Disorders of Sphingolipid Metabolism,* p. 169.
  Ed. Aronson, S. M. and Volk, B. W. Oxford: Pergamon.
SWEELEY, C. C. & KLIONSKY, B. (1963). *J. biol. Chem.* **238**, PC 3148.
SWEELEY, C. C. & KLIONSKY, B. (1966). In *The Metabolic Basis of Inherited
  Disease.* Ed. Stanbury, J. B., Wyngaarden, J. B., and Fredrickson, D. S. 2nd
  ed. p. 618. New York: —McGraw-Hill.
VOLK, B. W., WALLACE, B. J., SCHNECK, L., & SAIFER, A. (1964). *Archs Path.* **78**,
  483.
YAMAKAWA, T., YOKOYAMA, S., & HANDA, N. (1963). *J. Biochem.* **53**, 28.

NEUROPATHOLOGICAL ASPECTS OF SOME CEREBRAL LIPIDOSES

R. M. NORMAN*

THE history of the lipidoses shows that most of the forms which have been separated from each other on histological grounds have later been shown to differ sharply in their chemical features. Simple neuropathological findings have thus become confirmed as diagnostic criteria in their own right. The neuro-pathologist can also draw attention to certain features of these diseases for which as yet there is no chemical explanation. It was Klenk himself who remarked at the Lisbon Neurological Congress in 1953 that 'many of the questions put to the chemist by the neuropathologist can't be answered yet' and this is still true although the areas of uncertainty are rapidly shrinking.

Metachromatic leucodystrophy or sulphatide lipidosis

The late infantile form has been more extensively studied than the rarer juvenile and adult variants. The characteristic pathological finding is the accumulation in the demyelinated white matter of large amounts of material staining metachromatically with basic polychrome dyes and it was this feature which prompted Einarson & Neel in 1938 to classify their adult case separately from other degenerative conditions of the white matter. Other important features are that in spite of the severe myelin defect there is little or no sudanophil lipid in the tissues, and there may also be a striking absence of oligodendroglial nuclei.

It took longer to establish the point that similar staining material was also regularly found in many of the nerve cells, especially those of the dentate nucleus, and of the basal ganglia and brainstem. This was probably because early observers may not have used frozen sections, which are essential if metachromasia is to be shown properly, and partly because the lipid may have been confused with lipochrome pigment which may also stain metachromatically. However, the gross distension of many of the nerve cells with metachromatic lipid in my juvenile case of 1949 clearly related the condition to the lipidoses and further evidence of a widespread disorder was shown by the storage of metachromatic lipid in the kidney and gall bladder.

In 1955, von Hirsch & Peiffer introduced a simple and reliable method of demonstrating the abnormal lipid by acidified cresyl violet which stains the material a golden brown colour. This method showed that several cases, notably those of Scholz (1925), which had previously been classified

*Dr. Norman died in August, 1968.

as leucodystrophy with so-called 'pre-lipoid' deposits in the white matter, were in reality examples of the metachromatic type. Since then, the demonstration of brown metachromasia by this means has been regarded as essential for diagnosis.

Histologically, therefore, the condition appeared to be a lipid storage disease and this was first chemically proved by Jatzkewitz who, in 1958, showed that the tissues contained a large excess over normal of sulphatide.

Another very important neuropathological feature was added to the picture by Thieffry & Lyon (1959) who found metachromatic lipid in the peripheral nerves, both in Schwann cells and in phagocytes (Fig. 1).

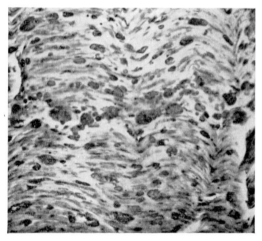

FIG. 1

Metachromatic leucodystrophy. Sciatic nerve
showing lipid deposits. Tolindine blue.

Peripheral nerve biopsy has since been confirmed as a valuable diagnostic procedure and should be carried out in preference to cerebral biopsy if the clinical investigations give rise to any uncertainty. The classical paper on the late infantile form is that of Brain & Greenfield (1950) and this condition may properly be called 'Greenfield's disease' (Jervis, 1958). There were also combined histological and chemical studies published in the early 1960s (Hagberg et al., 1960; Norman et al., 1960; Lyon et al., 1961) and the chemistry of the condition was further explored by Mehl & Jatzkewitz (1965) in Germany and by Austin et al. (1965) in America in a series of investigations which eventually led to the identification of the enzymatic abnormality responsible for the disease.

This subject has now been so thoroughly studied from the pathological and chemical points of view that it might be thought that all its mysteries had been revealed. But there have recently been 3 reported cases of a curious combination of metachromatic leucodystrophy in conjunction with a different type of lipidosis in the nerve cells of the cerebral cortex (Mossakowski *et al.*, 1961; Luthy *et al.*, 1965). The nerve cells in this situation did not stain metachromatically but were thought to resemble those of juvenile amaurotic idiocy. Nerve cells in the basal ganglia and brainstem, on the other hand, stained metachromatically as in the classical condition. These children showed hepatosplenomegaly which is not a feature of amaurotic family idiocy or of metachromatic leucodystrophy and further chemical investigation is needed to identify this condition more precisely.

DISEASES WITH PREDOMINANT STORAGE OF GANGLIOSIDE

Tay-Sachs disease has been so thoroughly studied that I will confine myself to two of its aspects: the changes in the cerebellum and in the white matter. The Purkinje cells share in the generalized neuronal lipidosis and storage of lipid is regularly seen, not only in the enlarged cell bodies but in the dendrites (Fig. 2). It is not so well known that the form taken by these

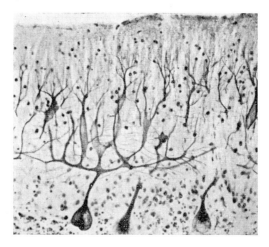

FIG. 2

Tay-Sachs disease. Cerebellum, showing swollen cell bodies and dendrites of the Purkinje cells. Gros-Bielschowsky.

cactus-like dendritic expansions differ from those commonly seen in gargoylism, which is another disease in which there are proved chemical abnormalities of ganglioside metabolism. The dendritic expansions in gargoylism characteristically appear as large clear-cut spherical or ovoid swellings and their lipid contents often show different staining reactions from those in the cell bodies (Fig. 3). These formations were well illustrated

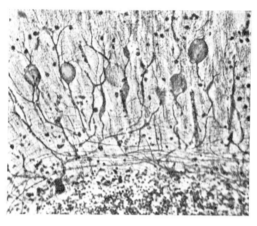

FIG. 3

Gargoylism. Spherical dendritic swellings.
Gros-Bielschowsky.

in Jervis's paper of 1950. I have seen this appearance in 4 cases of gargoylism and believe it to be of diagnostic value.

As regards the changes in the white matter in Tay-Sachs' disease, it has been known for many years that in contrast to the atrophied brains described in most of the classical cases, very heavy brains might occasionally be found at autopsy in patients who had shown all the usual clinical features of the disease, and that these brains were grossly demyelinated. The natural history of this aspect of the condition has been put into perspective by Aronson et al. (1958) in their study of 50 cases of Tay-Sachs disease. They showed that a progressive expansion of the brain took place after about the first year and that this change was associated with a progressive degeneration and an exuberant gliosis of the centrum ovale, and that a condition of megalencephaly was found in children who died during or after the third year.

The only other lipidoses in which enlargement of the head occurs is late infantile metachromatic leucodystrophy in which an analagous, though much less massive, swelling of the white matter takes place, and gargoylism, in which hydrocephalus may follow thickening of the leptomeninges.

In 1964, Landing et al. described a form of storage disease which differed from Tay-Sachs disease and to which they gave the non-committal name of 'familial neurovisceral lipidosis'. Landing described 8 infants from 6 families, all of whom had died before the age of 21 months, having shown mental and motor retardation. A cherry red spot at the macula had been seen in two. The brain showed changes similar to those of Tay-Sachs disease but the condition was regarded as a different entity because there was gross hepatosplenomegaly and because there were skeletal changes closely resembling those previously described by Caffey (1951), in what he had considered to be a precocious form of gargoylism. The condition was evidently similar to what I had in 1958 called 'Tay-Sachs disease with visceral involvement' before the chromatography of gangliosides was available. As in Landing's cases, the changes in the visceral organs were characterized by widespread involvement of the reticulo-endothelial system and also vacuolation of parenchymal cells, notably in the liver (Fig. 4) and glomerular epithelium of the kidney (Fig. 5). This condition

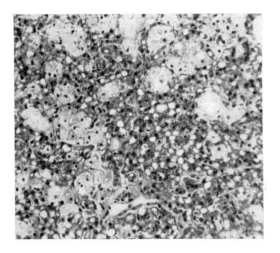

FIG. 4
'Generalised gangliosidosis'. Liver showing vacuolated hepatic cells and groups of paler foam cells. H. and E.

was defined chemically by O'Brien in 1965 who demonstrated that the lipid stored in brain and, to a less extent, in the liver and spleen, was not the Tay-Sachs ganglioside GM2 but the more slowly migrating GM1 of Svennerholm. My own case has since been shown by chromatography to belong to this new group.

Another European case has been that of Farkas-Bargeton (1965). Both her case and mine differed from Landing's in that the visceral histiocytes

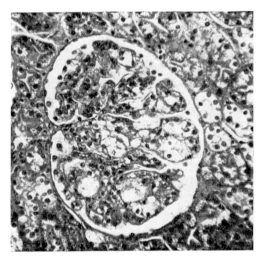

Fig. 5
'Generalised gangliosidosis'. Vacuolation of a
renal glomerulus. Blue trichrome.

and vacuolated parenchymal cells appeared entirely empty in formalin
fixed material whereas in Landing's cases some lipid had been found. Also.
the bony abnormalities were much less prominent.

Niemann-Pick disease

The infantile form presents an almost stereotyped picture in which lipid
is found in the nerve cells, in the visceral foam cells, and in the parenchyma
of glandular organs, indeed often in almost every tissue of the body. This
lipid stains black with haematoxylin after preliminary dichromate mordant-
ing as with myelin stains or with Baker's acid haematin (Fig. 6).

So far as the brain is concerned, there is often some overlap with histochemical findings in Tay-Sachs disease, despite the differences in the
preponderantly stored lipids. In the days before Klenk's chemical dis-
coveries, there was prolonged controversy as to whether or not Tay-Sachs
disease was the purely cerebral form of Niemann-Pick disease. Schaffer
(1930) was convinced that the diseases were different and many of his
simple histological points of distinction have since been verified. Thus, in
Niemann-Pick disease, there is lipid storage in the arachnoidal cells (Fig. 7)
and vascular endothelium. The cerebellar changes are also different in the
two conditions. In the Niemann-Pick cerebellum there is a prominent row
of intensely haematoxyphil microglial cells lying amid the Purkinje cells

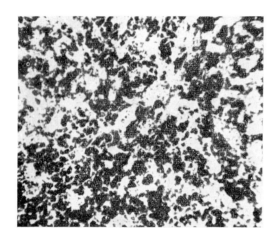

FIG. 6

Niemann-Pick disease. Lipid in the liver cells
and foam cells. Baker.

FIG. 7

Niemann-Pick disease. Arachnoidal cells
filled with lipid. Kultschitsky-Pal.

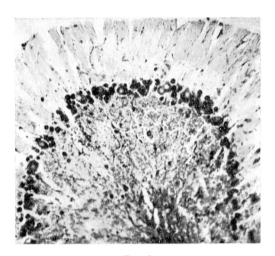

FIG. 8

Niemann-Pick disease. Cerebellum. Haematoxyphil lipid in the Purkinje cells and in numerous adjacent microglial cells. Kultischitsky-Pal.

(Fig. 8) which is not found in Tay-Sachs disease. The fact that these microglial cells appear regularly in areas where there is no detectable loss of
nerve cells suggests that they may store lipid as a primary process, not
simply by phagocytosis of material derived from neuronal degeneration.

In infantile Niemann-Pick disease there is an excess of sphingomyelin
in the white matter just as there is in the cerebral cortex. Presumably the
myelin sheaths are abnormally constituted and certainly they may show
degenerative changes. Myelin pallor and gliosis have been commonly
reported in the centrum ovale, but enlargement of the brain as in Tay-
Sachs disease has never been seen. In my case a true demyelination, that is
destruction of the myelin sheaths with sparing of the axis cylinders, was
present in the dentate nucleus and superior cerebellar peduncle.

INFANTILE GAUCHER'S DISEASE

It has been known since Rusca's paper in 1921 that widespread acute
neuronal degeneration is the main neuropathological feature of this condition which de Lange (1940) aptly called the malignant form of Gaucher's
disease. Schairer (1948) was the first to demonstrate lipid in some of the
nerve cells in his two cases. In my own example of the condition (Norman
et al., 1956), there were swollen nerve cells, obviously lipidotic, in the
thalamus and especially in the hippocampus (Fig. 9). These contained an
easily soluble P.A.S. positive material and similar staining was often seen

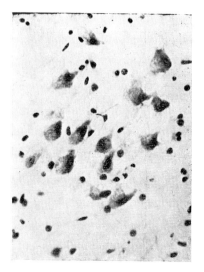

FIG. 9

Infantile Gaucher's disease. Lipidosis of nerve cells in
the hippocampal gyrus. Carbol azure.

elsewhere in less swollen cells. We suggested that whether or not neuronal
lipidosis appeared was dependent upon the varying severity of the metabolic
disturbance in the nerve cells. If the metabolic upset is sufficiently severe it
will lead to rapid cell death, while a less affected cell will survive long
enough for the products of disordered lipid metabolism to accumulate.
Since that time, the neuronal storage of lipid has been abundantly confirmed, notably by Banker *et al.* (1962) and by Seitelberger (1964) though
these changes have not always been present in other cases. Banker has
revived the suggestion made by Schairer that the presumed cerebroside in
the nerve cells is highly toxic and leads to rapid cell death, but this seems
improbable if only because in the juvenile case of Gaucher's disease which
was described by Maloney & Cummings (1960) there was little or no
neuronal loss despite ubiquitous lipidosis. In this case, there was chemical
proof of the accumulation of an abnormal glucocerebroside in the brain.

There is at present no chemical proof that in the infantile form cerebroside does, in fact, accumulate in nerve cells but there is evidence that this
lipid is stored in the swollen vascular adventitial cells that have almost
always been found since Debré *et al.* first described them in 1951 (Fig. 10).
What is surprising is that this pathognomonic finding was described so late
in the history of the disease, for the adventitial, Gaucher-like cells are

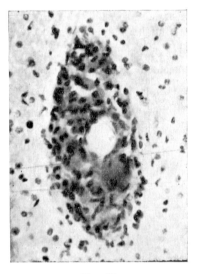

FIG. 10

Infantile Gaucher's disease. Lipidosis of vascular adventitial cells in cerebral white matter. P.A.S. and haematoxylin.

usually obvious enough in routine sections.. Perhaps the reason is that these formations are usually not numerous and are very patchily distributed in the white matter, so that large survey sections are more likely to reveal them. Svennerholm & Sourander (1965) found that tissue rich in these formations contained a high proportion of glucocerebroside which is not a constituent of the normal brain. However, it is not known whether these abnormal perivascular cells derive their cerebroside content from the brain or from the blood. Somewhat similar perivascular formations of so-called globoid cells are found in abundance in Krabbe's leucodystrophy but in Gaucher's disease they are not associated with degeneration of the myelin. Indeed they were absent from the extensively degenerated superior cerebellar peduncle in my case. Thus the perivascular cells are not dependent upon myelin breakdown for their lipid content. It seems to me unlikely that in Gaucher's disease this phenomenon can be explained purely as one of phagocytosis of cerebroside by normal cells for the phenomenon was not seen in the juvenile case of Maloney & Cummings although this brain contained abnormal glucocerebroside. The possibility remains that the adventitial cells are enzymatically abnormal, just as the visceral reticulo-endothelial cells certainly are.

REFERENCES

ARONSON, S. M., LEWITAN, A., RABINER, A., EPSTEIN, A. M., & VOLK, B. W. (1958). *A.M.A. Archs Neurol.* **79**, 151.

AUSTIN, J. H., ARMSTRONG, D. & SHEARER, L., (1965). *A.M.A. Archs. Neurol.* **13**, 593.

BANKER, B. Q., MILLER, J. Q., & CROCKER, A. C. (1962). In *Cerebral Sphingolipidoses* p. 73. Ed. Aronson, S. M. and Volk, B. W., New York: Academic Press.

BRAIN, W. R. & GREENFIELD, J. G. (1950). *Brain*, **73**, 291.

CAFFEY, J. (1951). *Bull. Hosp. Jt. Dis., N.Y.* **12**, 38.

DEBRÉ, R., BERTRAND, I., GRUMBACH, R., & BARGETON, E. (1951). *Archs fr. Pediat.* **8**, 38.

DE LANGE, C. (1940). *Acta paediat. Stockh.* **27**, 34.

EINARSON, L. & NEEL, A. V. (1938). *Acta Jutland*, **10**, 1.

FARKAS-BARGETON, E. (1965). *Proc. 5th Internat. Congr. Neuropath.* Zurich, 135.

HAGBERG, B., SOURANDER, P., SVENNERHOLM, L., & VOSS, H. (1960. *Acta pediat., Stockh.* **49**, 135.

JATZKEWITZ, H. (1958). *Hoppe-Seyler's Z. physiol. Chem.* **311**, 279.

JERVIS, G. (1950). *Archs Neurol. Psychiat., Chicago* **63**, 681.

KLENK, E. (1953). *Proc. 5th Int. Neurol. Congr.* Lisbon. Vol. 1, p. 253.

LANDING, H. G., SILVERMAN, F. N., CRAIG, J. M., JACOBY, M. D., LAHEY, M. E., & CHADWICK, D. L. (1964). *Amer. J. Dis. Child.* **108**, 503.

LUTHY, F., ULRICH, J., REGLI, F., & ISLER, W. (1965). *Proc. 5th Internat. Congr. Neuropath.* Zurich, 125.

LYON, G., ARTHUIS, M., & THIEFFRY, S. (1961). *Revue neurol.* **104**, 508.

MALONEY, A. F. J. & CUMMINGS, J. N. (1960). *J. Neurol. Neurosurg. Psychiat.* **23**, 207.

MEHL, E. & JATZKEWITZ, H. (1965). *Biochem. biophys. Res. Commun.* **19**, 407.

MOSSAKOWSKI, M., MATHIESON, G., & CUMMINGS, J. N. (1961). *Brain* **84**, 585.

NORMAN, R. M. (1949). *Brain* **70**, 234.

NORMAN, R. M., URICH, H., & LLOYD, O. C. (1956). *J. Path. Bact.* **78**, 409.

NORMAN, R. M., URICH, H., & TINGEY, A. H. (1960). *Brain* **83**, 369.

NORMAN, R. M., URICH, H., TINGEY, A. H., & GOODBODY, R. A. (1958). *J. Path. Bact.* **78**, 409.

O'BRIEN, J. S., STERN, M. B., LANDING, B. J., O'BRIEN, J. K., & DONNELL, G. (1965). *Am. J. Dis. Child.* **109**, 338.

RUSCA, L. C. (1921). *Haematologica,* **2**, 441.

SCHAFFER, K. (1930). *Archs Neurol. Psychiat.* **24**, 765.

SCHAIRER, E. (1948). *Virchows Arch. path. Anat. Physiol.* **315**, 395.

SCHOLZ, W. (1925). *Z. ges. Neurol. Psychiat.* **99**, 651.

SEITELBERGER, F. (1964). *Arch. Psychiat. NervKrankh.* **206**, 419

SVENNERHOLM, L. & SOURANDER, P. (1965). *Proc. 5th Int. Congr. Neuropath.* Zurich, 342.

THIEFFRY, S. & LYON, G. (1959). *Revue neurol.* **100**, 452.

VON HIRSCH, T. & PEIFFER, J. (1955). *Arch. Psychiat. NervKrankh.* **194**, 88.

DISCUSSION OF PRESENTATIONS BY
DR. NORMAN AND DR. RAINE

Wilson (London). Dr. Raine drew our attention to the structural changes in the lipid. Was he inferring that some of the conditions under discussion today might be due to structural abnormality? In the light of Dr. Norman's discussion what are the speakers' views on whether the conditions are due to an abnormal lipid in an otherwise normal brain or are the conditions due to a degeneration of the brain?

Norman. I do not really know about this. There is some doubt in some cases as to whether there is a cerebroside abnormality. Certainly in some infantile and childhood cases the cerebroside is abnormal in the brain and in the spleen.

Raine. This is one of the things we know little about at the moment. The question has been raised that some brain disorders may result from babies being fed on milk with an unusual sugar content, resulting in the formmation of abnormal lipids in the brain. I do not think this is likely. Should structural abnormalities occur they would have relatively greater effect if they occurred in the nerve cells rather than in the myelin sheath.

Norman. Gangliosides do not appear in the myelin sheath. In Niemann-Pick's disease the white matter might be normally formulated but there is an increase in sphingomyelin. Is the myelin sheath abnormal or is it normally constituted but tends to breakdown? Most of the electron micrographic studies in these lipidoses have been confined to the nerve cells. Is it suggested that the myelin is abnormal? The problem is not confined to the lipidoses but concerns the leucodystrophies.

Wilson. The fact that the disease does not appear until later suggests that the 'neuroaxis' is functioning normally and that the myelin sheath is abnormal.

Raine. I accept this. I have a rather crude view of the myelin sheath. It seems that subtle changes in the intimate structure of myelin are not going to affect the function of the neurone very much. On the other hand it may well be that the intimate structure of the nerve cells is far more important. The intra-cellular particles too have membranes round them which are essential for their proper function and small changes in these could have a profound effect.

CEREBRAL SPHINGOLIPIDOSES AS INBORN ERRORS OF METABOLISM

H. JATZKEWITZ

OUR biochemical investigation of the cerebral sphingolipidoses began in the following way. Among the collection of brains in our institute there were several from children who died of a disease which was described histologically in detail by Scholz in 1925. The disease lasts usually one to three years from the onset of the first clinical symptoms to death. It is characterized by an almost complete breakdown of myelin. As this disintegration should be caused by a disorder in nutrition of white matter the disease was called 'leucodystrophy, Type Scholz'. In contrast to normal myelin which is stained violet by the basic aniline dye cresyl violet, the degraded myelin was stained brown (Hirsch & Peiffer, 1955). Such a change in the absorption spectrum of a dye on combination with tissue elements was called 'metachromasia' by Ehrlich and hence the disease became known as 'metachromatic leucodystrophy'.

In order to discover the substance responsible for the metachromasia, lipid extracts of pathological white matter were prepared, spotted on to filter paper, and stained like tissue slices. It could be shown that the acetone and ether insoluble lipid constituents of the pathological white matter was stained brown whereas that from normal white matter was not. This made it possible to identify the lipids responsible for metachromasia by chromatographic and chemical methods (Jatzkewitz, 1958, 1960). They were cerebroside sulphates and their amount in pathological tissues was two to five times that in controls. Cerebroside sulphates are also termed 'sulphatides' and so the disease was recently renamed 'sulphatidosis. The change in its nomenclature reflects the advance in its investigation. It was however surprising that the accumulation of specific lipids in nervous tissue should give rise to a disintegration of specific neural structures.

Brain lipids

In the brain three lipid classes predominate (Fig. 1). The first consists of a single substance, cholesterol. The second is represented by the glycerophosphatides (e.g. phosphatidylcholine, phosphatidylethanolamine, the corresponding plasmalogens etc.). In this group the acceptor for the hydrophobic fatty acid residues is a small water soluble molecule, glycerol. The third class consists of the sphingolipids. In this group the acceptor for the hydrophobic fatty acid residue is the hydrophobic fatty amino-alcohol sphingosine. The total hydrophobic part of the sphingolipids is termed 'ceramide'. The hydrophilic part is attached to the primary terminal

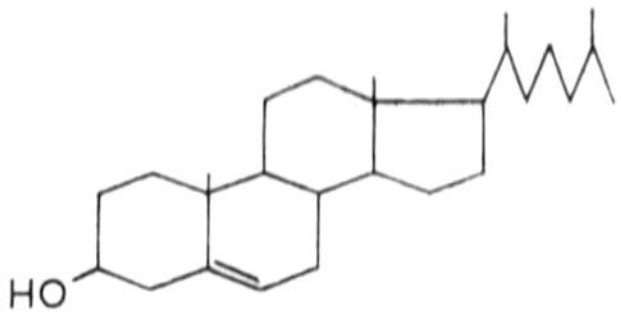

CHOLESTEROL

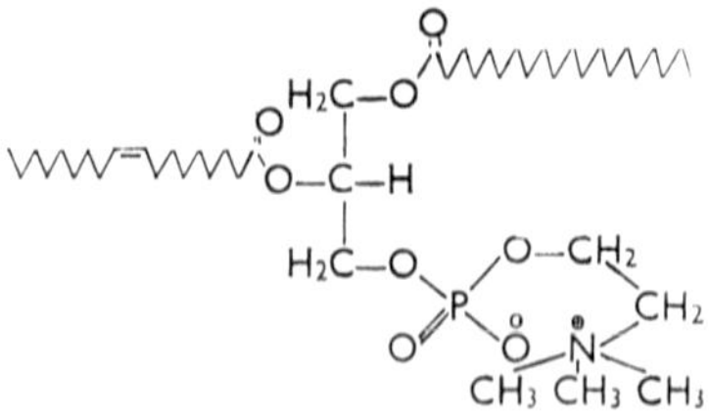

Phosphatidyl-choline (=Lecithin)

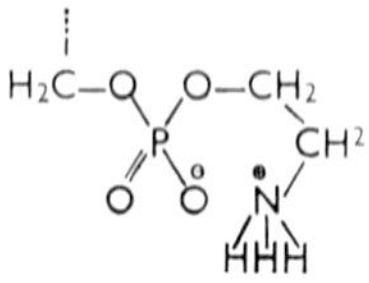

Phosphatidyl-ethanolamine
(= Cephalin)

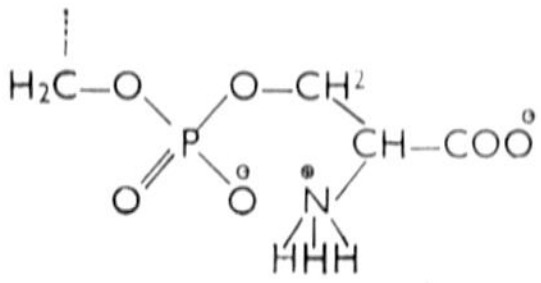

Phosphatidyl-serine

GLYCERO-PHOSPHATIDES

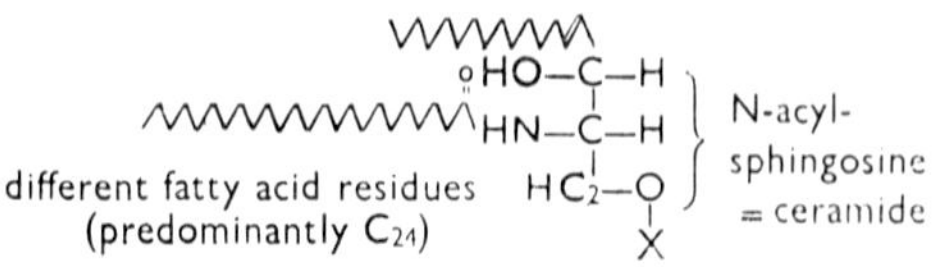

different fatty acid residues
(predominantly C_{24})

N-acyl-
sphingosine
= ceramide

sphingo-
glyco-
lipids

$X=$ galactose (in brain)   = galactocerebroside
    = glucose (e.g. in spleen)   = glucocerebroside
    = galactose-3-sulphate   = cerebroside sulphate
                                 (= sulphatide)
    = oligosaccharide   = ceramide oligosaccharide
    = oligosaccharide   = gangliosides
      +N-acetyl-
      neuraminic acid

sphingo-
phospho-
lipids

    = phosphoryl choline   = sphingomyelin

SPHINGOLIPIDS

Fig. 1
Predominant lipid classes in brain.

Sphingolipids

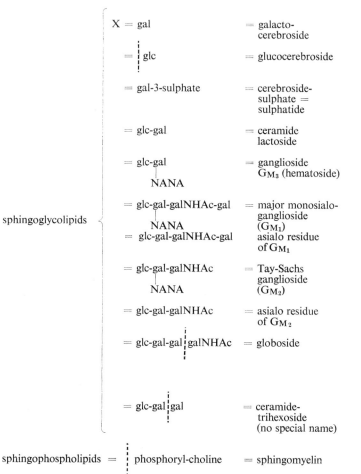

FIG. 2—Chemical classification of sphingolipids, and of diseases caused by their accumulation due to enzyme deficiency (⋮).

Disease caused by accumulation	predominant localization of accumulated substances	enzyme deficiency (where known)
Gaucher's disease	visceral organs (sometimes brain)	glucocerebrosidase
metachromatic leucodystrophy	brain (whitematter), kidney	cerebroside sulphatase and arylsulphatase A
exceptional cases of amaurotic idiocy (AI) with visceral involvement	brain (gray matter), visceral organs	
exceptional cases of AI with visceral involvement	brain (gray matter), visceral organs	
usual cases of AI (Tay-Sachs-disease) with predominant storage of ganglioside G_{M_2}	brain (gray matter)	
exceptional cases of Tay-Sachs-disease with visceral involvement	brain (gray matter) visceral organs	globoside and asialo residue of G_{M_1} cleaving hexosaminidase
Fabry's disease	kidney (other visceral organs and brain); clinically skin	ceramide-trihexoside cleaving galactosidase
Niemann-Pick disease	brain (gray matter) visceral organs	sphingomyelinase

glc = glucose; gal = galactose; galNHAc = galactosamine;
NANA = N-acetyl-neuraminic acid = sialic acid; asialo = NANA-free.

hydroxyl group of sphingosine. This consists either of a sugar residue or an oligosaccharide chain with or without N-acetyl-neuraminic acid or phosphorylcholine.

Pathological Accumulation

It is noteworthy that, in contrast to the glycerophosphatides, nearly every sphingolipid is known to accumulate pathologically in man leading to the diseases listed in Fig. 2, which includes metachromatic leucodystrophy. An exception is when the hydrophilic part is galactose, as in the galactocerebrosides of brain, where no pathological accumulation is known. Usually the clinical onset of these rare diseases is in early childhood. Nearly all cases show involvement of the nervous system and in many, the visceral organs are also affected. Gaucher's, Tay-Sachs', and Niemann-Pick disease are predominantly restricted to Jewish families.

Enzyme defects

All these diseases, which are of lifelong duration, follow the recessive mode of inheritance. They are 'inborn errors of metabolism' in the sense used by Garrod and he suggested that such diseases arise because an enzyme governing a single metabolic step is reduced in activity or missing altogether. For a review see Stanbury, Wyngaarden & Fredrickson (1966).

The question then arises as to how a deficiency of an enzyme can lead to an accumulation of an end product of metabolism. The answer is connected with the well-known fact that the organism is no static being. Even what seems to be unchangeable as a morphologic structure, is the result of balance between biosynthesis and degradation of the substances forming the structure. Biosynthesis and degradation of a substance are regulated by different enzymes and so there are two possibilities leading to an increased amount of a substance in a tissue: an activation of the anabolic enzyme or an inactivation of the catabolic one. On the principle of one gene, one enzyme a genetic defect could only result in an accumulation of substrate by causing a defect in its catabolic enzyme. This seems to be true for all known inborn errors of metabolism with recessive inheritance e.g., phenylketonuria, galactosaemia, maple syrup urine disease etc. and the same seems to be true for the sphingolipidoses.

Thus Brady, Kanfer & Shapiro (1965) and Patrick (1965) have shown that in spleens from patients with Gaucher's disease there is a deficiency of a glucocerebrosidase, an enzyme which cleaves glucocerebroside into ceramide and glucose:

$$\text{ceramide-glucose} \atop (= \text{glucocerebroside}) \xrightarrow[\textit{cerebrosidase}]{\textit{gluco-}} \text{ceramide} + \text{glucose}$$

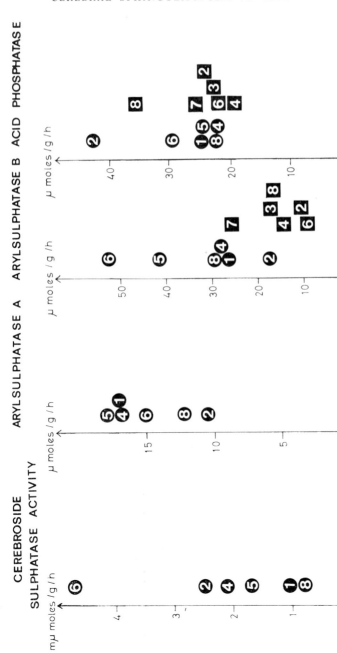

FIG. 3

Deficiency of arylsulfatase A and its cerebroside sulfatase activity in renal cortex in cases of metachromatic leukodystrophy.

At about the same time Mehl & Jatzkewitz (1965) found that in kidney of patients dying of metachromatic leukodystrophy, cerebroside sulphatase was absent. This enzyme cleaves cerebroside sulphates (sulphatides) into cerebroside and sulphate:

$$\text{Cerebroside sulphate} \atop (= \text{sulphatide}) \quad \xrightarrow[\text{sulphatase}]{\text{cerebroside}} \quad \text{cerebroside} + \text{sulphate}$$

Apparently contrary to the assumption of a single enzyme block in this disease, Austin *et al.* (1963) found that an enzyme (arylsulphatase A) which splits arylsulphates

$$\text{2-hydroxy-5-nitrophenyl} \atop (= \text{p-nitrocatechol}) \text{ sulphate} \quad \xrightarrow{\text{aryl-}\atop\text{sulphatase A}}$$

2-hydroxy-5-nitrophenol + sulphate
(= p-nitrocatechol)

was also markedly diminished in brain and kidney in cases of metachromatic leukodystrophy. This discrepancy has however been resolved since arylsulphatase A has been shown to be a component of the cerebroside sulphatase (Mehl & Jatzkewitz, 1964).

As a deficiency of cerebroside sulphatase was originally demonstrated in only one pathological case compared with two controls I wish to show in Fig. 3 the extension of this work using tissues from 6 patients and 6 controls. Arylsulphatase B and acid phosphatase activity were determined in order to demonstrate to what extent the tissues were enzymatically intact. This was necessary since all samples were obtained by autopsy and stored in a refrigerator sometimes for years. It was difficult to obtain them since the usual storage of organs in formalin destroys their enzymatic activity. I should like to thank Dr. Austin, Dr. Cumings, Dr. Lowenthal and Dr. Peiffer for the provision of these rare samples.

Further evidence for a defect in the catabolic enzyme was obtained by investigating liver, kidney and spleen from patients with Niemann-Pick disease, a sphingomyelin-lipidosis. Brady, Kanfer, Mock & Fredrickson (1966) and later Schneider & Kennedy (1967) found that sphingomyelinase activity was markedly diminished in liver and spleen of these patients compared with controls. The enzyme hydrolyses sphingomyelin according to the following scheme:

$$\text{ceramide-phosphorylcholine} \atop (= \text{sphingomyelin}) \quad \xrightarrow[\text{myelinase}]{\text{sphingo-}} \quad \text{ceramide} + \text{phosphoryl-} \atop \text{choline}$$

Familial amaurotic idiocy

Our own investigations were directed to familial amaurotic idiocy or in terms of substances, to the accumulation of gangliosides and their neuraminic acid-free (asialo-) residues (Fig. 4). Normal brain contains only

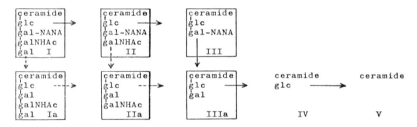

FIG. 4

Scheme for the biological degradation of the monosialogangliosides in brain.

gangliosides of the tetrasaccharide type in significant amounts, particularly gangliosides with one (I), two or three N-acetyl-neuraminic acid residues. On the other hand, in cases of Tay-Sachs disease the monosialoceramide-trisaccharide II is strikingly increased (Svennerholm, 1962). We have detected three biochemically exceptional cases, one of which will not be mentioned until later. In the first, a late infantile case, the major monosialoganglioside I had accumulated (Jatzkewitz & Sandhoff, 1963). In the second, an infantile case, the ceramide-disaccharide IIIa, the corresponding ganglioside III and Tay-Sachs ganglioside II were increased in the ratio 10:2:3 (Pilz, Sandhoff & Jatzkewitz, 1966). The accumulation of a ganglioside was always accompanied by an accumulation of the corresponding neuraminic acid-free residue.

Thus in three biochemically different forms of infantile amaurotic idiocy three different pairs of substances are accumulated which in Fig. 4 are marked by boxes (storage of I and Ia, II and IIa, III and IIIa). The accumulation of I and Ia and III and IIIa leads also to visceral involvement. The third exceptional case, which is not demonstrated in the scheme, will be mentioned later.

With the one gene/one enzyme principle in mind and assuming a deficiency of the catabolic enzyme it is possible to suggest a scheme for the physiological degradation of the monosialogangliosides in brain and for metabolic blocks in the pathological cases. For this purpose it is necessary

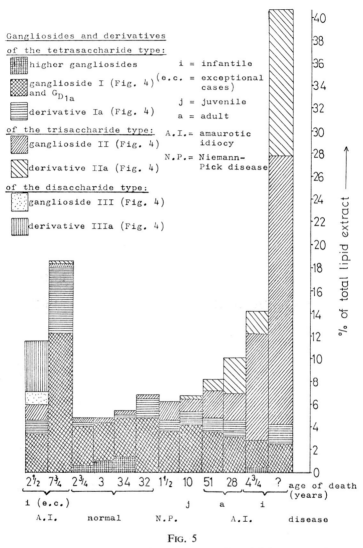

FIG. 5

Gangliosides and derivatives in percentages of total lipid extract of grey matter in controls and different forms of amaurotic idiocy.

to compare quantitatively the amount of the biogenetically related compounds in the normal and pathological tissues, as shown in Fig. 5 (Jatzkewitz, Pilz, & Sandhoff, 1965). This was established by an ultramicromethod following separation by thin layer chromatography and led the assumption that two pathways of monosialoganglioside degradation may exist. One proceeds via the lower ganglioside homologues (solid arrows), the other, via the neuraminic acid-free residues (interrupted arrows). The strong accumulation of gangliosides in cases of infantile amaurotic idiocy and their different quantitative patterns in the different disease forms, strongly supports the pathway via the lower gangliosides. On the other hand the accumulation of the corresponding neuraminic acid-free residues and their enzymatic degradation, though small in brain, gives evidence for the pathway via the neuraminic acid-free compounds. Thus it seems that the first pathway mentioned is preferred but that possibly both are used.

This physiological scheme has been partly confirmed: Gatt and co-workers (see Gatt, 1967) have detected in normal brain all the enzymes which catalyze the particular steps in the degradation of the major mono-sialoganglioside I via the lower gangliosides (solid arrows) and the degradation of Ia to V. In our laboratory a crude enzyme preparation from kidney was obtained which catalyzes the degradation of Ia to V and another catalysing step III to IIIa (Sandhoff & Jatzkewitz, 1964, 1967).

Recently the enzyme deficiency in the gangliosidosis with the accumulation of the major monosialganglioside I and its neuraminic acid-free residue Ia in brain has been established. It is due to a lack of β-galactosidase in brain and in visceral organs (Okada & O'Brien, 1968). The enzyme deficiency is also known in an exceptional biochemical case of Tay-Sachs disease, the third variant which we detected (Sandhoff, Andreae, & Jatzkewitz, 1968). It was clinically typical of Tay-Sachs disease, a non-Jewish German boy with onset of symptons at 6 months and who died aged 25 months. A cherry-red spot in the macula and the other expected changes were present. In this case, however, not only Tay-Sachs ganglioside (II) and its asialo residue (IIa) had accumulated but in addition kidney globoside (VI) was present in the visceral organs (Fig. 6), the kidney showing marked histological changes.

Fig. 6 shows that the three glycolipids accumulated have in common N-acetyl-galactosamine (N-acetylhexosamine) not only in a similar terminal position of the oligosaccharide chain but also in the same chemical linkage. Thus it seems reasonable to assume a deficient N-acetyl-galactosaminidase (hexosaminidase) in this special case and this has been verified. This deficiency gives rise to the accumulation of the globoside VI and probably to the increased amount of the asialo residue IIa compared with the amount found in the usual cases. The first degradation product which is formed from the globoside VI by the action of the hexosaminidase is a ceramide-trisaccharide (ceramide-glc-gal-gal) which is pathologically accumulated, especially in kidney of patients with Fabry's disease, due to a deficiency of the ceramide-trisaccharide cleaving enzyme (Brady, Gal, Bradley, Warshaw, & Laster, 1967).

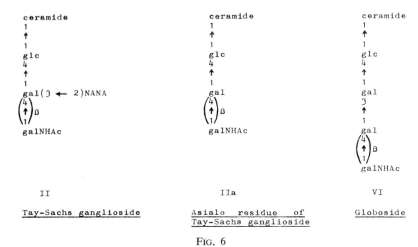

FIG. 6

Glycolipids accumulated in an exceptional case of Tay-Sachs disease. glc = glucose; gal = galactose; galNHAc = galactosamine; NANA = N-acetyl-neuraminic acid = sialic acid.

Thus the prediction that a deficiency of the catabolic enzyme directly produces the accumulation of its substrate seems to be justified probably in all cases with generalized sphingolipidoses. In the classical type of Tay-Sachs disease, however, with the preferential storage of Tay-Sachs ganglioside in nervous tissue, another mechanism may have to be involved.

Clinical aspects

The clinical symptoms of each of the sphingolipidoses can appear in children, young people, or adults. Accordingly, they are clinically divided into infantile, juvenile and adult forms. This clinical division does not necessarily correspond to the biochemical one. Fig. 5 shows that there is, for instance, in the case of juvenile amaurotic idiocy, a similar pattern of gangliosides and their derivatives to that seen in a case of Niemann-Pick disease, a sphingomyelin lipidosis. On the other hand, in at least one of the two adult cases there was an accumulation of these same glycolipids, so that this could be considered as a delayed form of the infantile Tay-Sachs disease.

This means that the clinical picture of amaurotic idiocy can be produced by different biochemical causes. In infantile cases it is most frequently due to an accumulation of ganglioside. On the other hand, substances as closely related as the different gangliosides can produce different clinical pictures. It is not however the aim of this biochemical review to use these facts to further the classification of the sphingolipidoses.

Biochemical diagnosis of sphingolipidoses can be performed using biopsy specimens from brain, peripheral nerve, rectum and, in cases with visceral involvement, from non-neural tissue. Metachromatic leucodystrophy can be recognized by investigating either the lipids (Austin, 1957) or the arylsulphatase A activity (Austin *et al.,* 1966) in urine or in small samples of venous blood (Percy & Brody, 1968). Diagnosis of Gaucher's disease and Niemann-Pick disease is also possible with small samples of venous blood using radioactive glucocerebroside and radioactive sphingomyelin, respectively, as substrates (Kampine, Brady, Kanfer, Feld, & Shapiro, 1967).

No specific therapy of the sphingolipidoses is available and it seems also highly improbable in future. The only thing that can be done is to develop methods for the detection of the heterozygous carriers, by which it should be possible to take eugenic care in families with a member suffering from a sphingolipidosis.

Open Questions

Finally I wish to draw attention to some open questions at the molecular level of sphingolipidoses. I began with metachromatic leucodystrophy as an example and I should like to return to this. The first patient from whom we determined the cerebroside sulphatase activity in kidney, with radioactive sulphatides as substrate had an enzyme activity less than 2 per cent of the controls. Surprisingly his first clinical symptoms appeared at the age of 17. He died at the age of 20. Accordingly the disease lasted clinically for 3 years. The same duration was seen in infantile cases. The question arises: has the patient lived without cerebroside sulphatase up to the age of 20? If not, it has to be assumed that this lack of enzyme or of its regulation occurred at some time during his life affecting all the organs where sulphatides play a role. This is difficult to explain in terms of the one gene/one enzyme, principle. This principle, however, refers to the structural gene, inducing directly the chemical structure of the corresponding enzyme.

If the structural gene is deficient then the induced structure of the enzyme is also deficient (Fig. 7, below). However, recently it has been shown in bacteria that the quantity of enzyme which is induced by the structural gene is controlled by control genes. If a control gene is deficient, (Fig. 7, above), then the structural gene has a normal chemical composition but its amount is changed. In this case a defect of the control gene could give rise to an overshoot in synthesis of its product. This has already been shown in one human disease, acute intermittent porphyria (Tschudi *et al.,* 1965). Nevertheless, in all sphingolipidoses so far investigated a deficient catabolic enzyme has been found, probably as a consequence of a deficient structural gene (Fig. 7, below). Brady's observation of some difference in the heat stability and substrate affinity of glucocere-

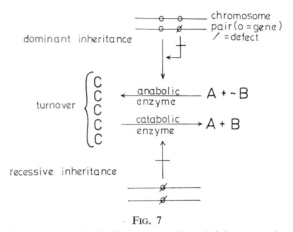

FIG. 7

Product accumulation in diseases caused by a deficient control gene
(above) or by a deficient structural gene (below). ($\sim$ B = activated
form of B).

brosidase preparations from spleens of patients with Gaucher's disease
compared with those from controls supports this assumption provided
that this effect was not simulated by other glucocerebrosidases in the same
tissue.

By analogy with inherited haemoglobin variants (the DNA of) the same
structural gene may mutate in different ways so that there may arise
enzymes of different structures with different catalytic activity. This would
presume that the structural gene though mutating rarely in these rare
diseases nevertheless mutates in different ways according to the age of
onset of clinical symptoms. Those where the catalytic site is severely
affected should give rise to infantile cases of the disease and those where
it is only slightly affected the juvenile and adult ones. It was to be expected
then that the residual activity of those enzymes causing product accumulation of the same biochemical origin in the same organ should be higher
with increasing age of clinical onset. However, in general this progression
has not been found either in our own or in other laboratories.

The second question is why, except in very rare cases of congenital
metachromatic leukodystrophy, the clinical symptoms of the disease
appear, at the earliest, with the end of myelination, about one year after
birth. Fig. 8 perhaps answers this question. It gives the preliminary results
of comparative investigations on the activity of the lysosomal acid phosphatase, arylsulphatase and cerebroside sulphatase in rabbit brain in
relation to age. It is to be seen that the activity of cerebroside sulphatase
constantly rises and reaches its maximum after the myelin sheath is mainly
completed, about 8 to 20 weeks after birth. Since this enzyme is concerned

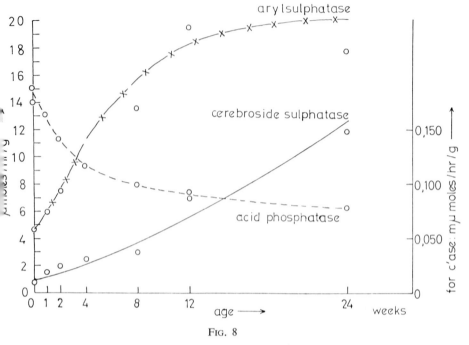

FIG. 8

Activity of three hydrolases in rabbit brain in relation to age (o = average of two determinations).

in the breakdown of cerebroside sulphate in brain, its deficiency will not be of significance before the completion of myelination.

Since nearly all sphingolipidoses are generalized disorders, death is mainly due to involvement of those organs where the turnover of the substances accumulated is highest, e.g. in the visceral organs in Niemann-Pick and Gaucher's disease. Death is also due to alteration of structures whose integrity is especially important for survival such as nervous tissue in amaurotic idiocy and in metachromatic leucodystrophy. Nevertheless the relatively long duration of the illness due to sphingolipidoses, even in children, probably depends on the low activity of the enzymes which are involved in sphingolipid turnover (see Fig. 8). A deficiency of these enzymes effects the accumulation of metabolites which are relatively inert and involved in physiologically specialized tasks. Probably therefore, the diseased patient survives for a longer time, allowing the storage of sphingolipids to appear clinically. The reason why no reliable case of glycerophosphatide storage is known, may well be because a similar deficiency of an enzyme involved in glycerophosphatide metabolism would either prevent the formation of an embryo or give rise to a premature abortion.

REFERENCES

AUSTIN, J. H. (1957). *Neurology, Minneap.* **7**, 415 and 716.
AUSTIN, J. H., ARMSTRONG, D., SHEARER, L., & MCAFEE, D. (1966). *Archs Neurol. Chicago,* **14**, 259.
AUSTIN, J. H., BALASUBRAMANIAN, A., PATTABIRAMAN, T., SARASWATHI, S., BASU, D., & BACHHAWAT, B. (1963). *J. Neurochem.* **10**, 805.
BRADY, R. O., GAL, A. E., BRADLEY, R. M., WARSHAW, A. L., & LASTER, L. (1967). *Fedn Proc. Fedn Am. Socs exp. Biol.* **26**, 277.
BRADY, R. O., KANFER, J. N., MOCK, M. B., & FREDRICKSON, D. S. (1966). *Proc. Nat. Acad. Sci. U.S.A.* **55**, 366.
BRADY, R. O., KANFER, J. N., & SHAPIRO, D. (1965). *Biochem. biophys. Res. Commun.* **18**, 221.
GATT, S. (1967). *Biochim. biophys. Acta,* **137**, 192.
HIRSCH, TH. V. & PEIFFER, J. (1955). *Arch. Psychiatrie,* **194**, 88.
JATZKEWITZ, H. (1958, 1960). *Hoppe-Seyler's Z. physiol. Chem.* **311**, 279; **318**, 265; **320**, 134.
JATZKEWITZ, H., PILZ, H., & SANDHOFF, K. (1965). *J. Neurochem.* **12**, 135.
JATZKEWITZ, H. & SANDHOFF, K. (1963). *Biochim. biophys. Acta* **70**, 354.
KAMPINE, J. P., BRADY, R. O., KANFER, J. N., FELD, M., & SHAPIRO, D. (1967). *Science, N.Y.* **155**, 86.
MEHL, E. & JATZKEWITZ, H. (1964). *Hoppe-Seyler's Z. physiol. Chem.* **339**, 260.
MEHL, E. & JATZKEWITZ, H. (1965). *Biochem. biophys. Res. Commun.* **19**, 407.
PATRICK, A. D. (1965). *Biochem. J.* **97**, 17C.
PERCY, A. K. & BRADY, R. O. (1968). *Science, N.Y.,* **161**, 594.
OKADA, S. &O'Brien, J. S. (1768). *Science, N.Y.,* **160**, 1002.
PILZ, H., SANDHOFF, K., & JATZKEWITZ, H. (1966). *J. Neurochem.* **13**, 1273.
SANDHOFF, K., ANDREAE, U., & JATZKEWITZ, H. (1968). *Life Sci.* **7**, 283.
SANDHOFF, K. & JATZKEWITZ, H. (1964). *Hoppe-Seyler's Z. physiol. Chem.* **338**, 281.
SANDHOFF, K. & JATZKEWITZ, H. (1967). *Biochim. biophys. Acta* **141**, 442.
SCHNEIDER, P. B. & KENNEDY, E. P. (1967). *J. Lipid Res.* **8**, 202.
SCHOLZ, W. (1925). *Z. Neurol.* **99**, 651.
STANBURY, J. B., WYNGAARDEN, J. B., & FREDRICKSON, D. S. (1966). *The Metabolic Basis of Inherited Disease,* 2nd. Ed. p. 4. New York: McGraw-Hill.
SVENNERHOLM, L. (1962). *Biochem. biophys. Res. Commun.* **9**, 436.
TSCHUDI, D. P., PERLROTH, M. G., MARRER, H. S., COLLINS, A., HUNTER, Jr., G., & RECHCIGL Jr., M. (1965). *Proc. Nat. Acad. Sci. U.S.A.,* **53**, 841.

DISCUSSION OF PRESENTATION BY DR. JATZKEWITZ

Raine (Birmingham). We cannot let this very detailed paper go by without comment. This was a remarkable account of a very fine piece of work. Would you expand on this Dr. Jatzkewitz and tell us whether we can apply these techniques to brain biopsies; is there any danger of the material decomposing and what is the method of extracting it?

Jatzkewitz. It is rather difficult but you have the advantage that the ganglioside is an acid substance. We make a lipid extract and use a combination of solvent systems on a thin layer plate, running in the same direction. Some solvent systems are basic and contain ammonia and, as the gangliosides are acid, they can be separated.

Campbell (London). Dr. Jatzkewitz is to be complimented on his presentation. Have the other organs of patients with Tay-Sachs disease shown any obvious abnormality? Do you have any suggestions concerning the nomenclature of Tay-Sachs and amaurotic family idiocy?

Jatzkewitz. On the first question—not much work has been done in respect of other organs but we have found evidence of abnormal lipid in the spleen and other viscera in small amounts in a few patients only. On the second question, it is better to use the names already given.

Roberts (Liverpool). On this point, three years ago I had a case of Tay Sachs in hospital. The nurse left the charts near the bed and the father read the diagnosis and was extremely upset when he looked up the term in the dictionary. Wouldn't it be better to use chemical classifications?

Raine. Dr. Jatzkewitz has suggested a chemical classification but I wonder how specific such a classification might be. Are we really yet getting at the basic defect in these disorders?

Jatzkewitz. It is very difficult to differentiate between amaurotic family idiocy and Niemann-Pick and they must all be kept in mind.

Norman (Bristol). One ventures into this question of classification with some trepidation. Either you have to have a chemical classification or you have to use the names of people discovering the disease. As a Pathologist I think the latter suggestion is, for the time being, the better one.

Stern (Carshalton). If you break down gangliosides successively you end up with glucocerebroside. What is the defect in Gaucher's disease?

Jatzkewitz. There are two enzymes involved in the breakdown of glucocerebrosides. One only attacks the glucocerebrosides. In cases not involving the brain but only the viscera there is a defect in the enzyme which breaks down this glucocerebroside and this is not involved in ganglioside breakdown. In a few infantile cases, however, where the brain is involved, I think there might be, in addition, a lack of this second enzyme. The visceral involvement that has been studied by Brady is really a deficiency in the enzyme which is involved in both the breakdown of glucocerebroside and ganglioside.

F

SOME OBSERVATIONS ON THE NATURAL HISTORY
OF WILSON'S DISEASE

J. M. WALSHE

I WISH to start this account of Wilson's disease by reviewing some of the genetic data recorded from 43 sibships in which the abnormal gene for this disease occurred. Since Bearn's (1960) analysis of 30 families collected in the New York area there has been no genetic analysis of Wilson's disease; as his families were largely collected from two highly inbred groups, the eastern Europen Jewish and the Sicilian communities of New York, the data obtained from his survey would not necessarily stand unmodified for families seen in the United Kingdom.

The 43 sibships I have studied are of the following racial origins, 27 were English stock, 3 Scottish, 3 eastern European Jews, 3 Greek, 1 Polish, 1 Italian, 1 Welsh, 1 Turkish: there were also 2 cross-breeds, 1 Welsh Italian and 1 Polish Scottish. In addition 1 patient was adopted so that his parents and other family relations are not known. These 43 sibships comprised 129 offspring. Amongst these there were six neonatal deaths in four families, the sex of the siblings was not recorded, and of the remainder 66 were males and 57 females. Of these 123 surviving children 2 died before the age of 5, and of the remaining 121 there were 60 cases of Wilson's disease, 30 in males with mean age of onset of 13·7 years and 30 cases amongst females, also with mean age of onset of 13·7 years. After subtracting the propositi from these 121 offspring no less than 17 of the remaining 78 were either proven or probable cases of Wilson's disease, thus the figure of 22 per cent so achieved approximates closely to the expected 25 per cent for a recessively inherited disease.

In Bearn's analysis of cases seen in New York there was a consanguinity rate among parents of 46·67%, the figure was much lower for the present series but was above average for the population in general as there were 4 first cousin marriages, 2 being between English parents, 1 Scottish and 1 Jewish. In addition there was 1 case arising from incest. This particular patient had an elder true brother who was not affected. Of these 43 sibships there was more than 1 child involved in 15, and in 2 families there were 3 affected individuals.

As a whole the disease tended to run true to type in families, so that if the first case presented with hepatic manifestation of the disease subsequent cases tended to do the same. Similarly if the first case was neurological later cases were neurological. In 6 families however the second case was diagnosed in the asymptomatic stage by biochemical screening of siblings. In 1 family the first two children died at the age of 8 of hepatic

Table I. *Age at onset of Wilson's disease.*

Family	1st sibling	Age 2nd sibling	3rd sibling
B	8	8	14
G	37†	37†	
H	7	10	
J	12	12	11
LeM	27	21*	
M	8	7*	
N	8	8	
R	12	9*	
T	12	10	
V	12	12	

* Diagnosis made in the asymptomatic stage.
† Age at death—age of onset not known.

failure whilst the third sibling was unaffected and the fourth presented with neurological disease at the age of 14. The age of onset also tended to be remarkably constant and is shown from Table I. Similarly the concentration of caeruloplasmin in the serum tended to run true to type in families, thus in 2 families when the propositus had an above average serum oxidase activity the same was found also for the asymptomatic younger sibling diagnosed on screening.

In general the search for the heterozygote in Wilson's disease depends on radiochemical studies (Sternlieb *et al.*, 1961), but this has also been carried out by estimating the serum oxidase activity (caeruloplasmin) in as many parents and close relatives as possible. The results (Fig. 1) indicate that a certain number of heterozygotes only can be picked up by this technique and negative findings do not exclude the carrier state for this condition. On the whole there appears to be no correlation between oxidase activity in the sera of close relatives and the findings in patients. Typical findings are shown in the D.R.W. family (Fig. 2).

The presenting symptoms of the various patients are shown in Table II. Three asymptomatic patients were diagnosed after the death of an elder sibling, the nature of the illness being identified at post-mortem examina-

Table II. *Presenting symptoms of Wilson's disease.*

Hepatic disease	28 cases (8 with haemolysis)
Nervous system disease	23 cases (1 schizophrenic)
Asymptomatic	6 cases (4 with abnormal liver function tests)
Fever, followed by signs of brain damage	2 cases
Rickets	1 case

RELATIVES OF PATIENTS WITH WILSON'S DISEASE

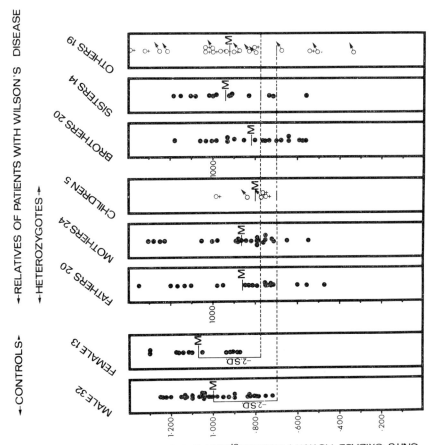

FIG. 1

Distribution of serum oxidase activity (caeruloplasmin) in control subjects and in close relatives of patients with Wilson's disease. The mean for each group is shown together with two standard deviations below the mean for the male and female controls.

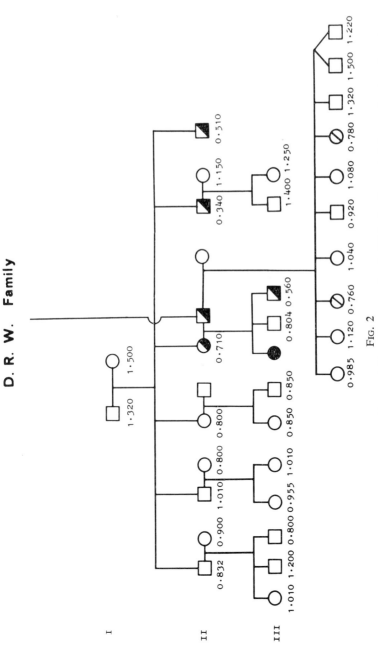

FIG. 2

The D. R. W. family. The figures represent oxidase activities. The propositus is III 8, the diagnosis being made at post-mortem examination so that her caeruloplasmin value was not known. The heterozygotes are marked as half hatched figures. Her father married again and had a further 10 children by his second wife, and two of these are marked as possible heterozygotes because their serum oxidase activities were nearly two standard deviations below the mean for female controls.

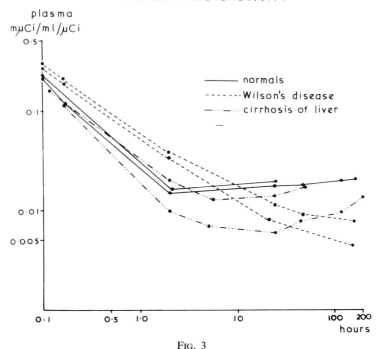

PLASMA RADIOACTIVITY

Fig. 3

Rate of disappearance of radiocopper (^{64}Cu or ^{67}Cu) from the plasma of two two patients with Wilson's disease compared with two normal controls and two patients with hepatic cirrhosis. Both radioactivity in plasma and the time are plotted on a logarithmic scale.

tion. In these cases the privileges that primogeniture conveys are somewhat doubtful and it appears still to be necessary in some families for the first child to be sacrificed so that a diagnosis can be made in subsequent siblings.

I would now like to pass on briefly to some conclusions that Osborn and I have recently drawn on the natural history of copper deposition in Wilson's disease as a result of our studies with radioactive copper. This work has been reported in some detail in the *Lancet* (Osborn & Walshe, 1967). During the 10 years we have been using ^{64}Cu the specific activity of the copper has varied considerably so that we have injected as little as 2·5 μg on the one hand and as much as 800 μg. Cu^{2+} on the other. It therefore seemed possible that our results may have been influenced by the amount of ionic copper in the injections. However when the uptake of ^{64}Cu by the liver at any given time is plotted against the μg. of ionic copper injected the results show that within this range (2·5-800 μg.) variation in specific activity has not influenced the results.

I must mention at this point the methods of diagnosis of asymptomatic siblings and patients with prolonged hepatic Wilson's disease. The Kayser Fleischer ring, if present, is always diagnostic, but in the early stages of the disease this may not be seen even on slit lamp examination of the cornea. In these cases we rely on a number of parameters such as family history, the amount of copper excreted in the urine, the relationship of the serum copper to the serum caeruloplasmin concentration (in Wilson's disease there is always a large discrepancy), the response of the urine copper to a test dose of penicillamine and the rate of incorporation of radiocopper into serum globulins.

The differences between controls, non-Wilsonian hepatic cases and patients with Wilson's disease are shown in Figure 3. After injection of radiocopper the first useful measure is the liver/thigh ratio studied over the first 15 minutes, and already there is a clear grouping to be seen between the controls and heterozygotes on the one hand and the advanced neurological cases of the Wilson's disease on the other showing the progressive inability of the liver to take up copper in the more advanced forms of the disease (Fig. 4). This point is similarly illustrated by studying the percentage dose present in the liver at both 2 hours and 24 hours after injection; it is

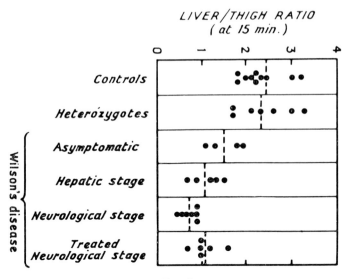

FIG. 4

The liver/thigh ratio at 15 minutes is shown in this diagram. The hetero-zygotes and controls have a strictly comparable ratio. This is reduced in the asymptomatic siblings, reduced even further in the hepatic stage o, Wilson's disease, and is very low in the neurological stage. After treat-ment there is a return towards normal.

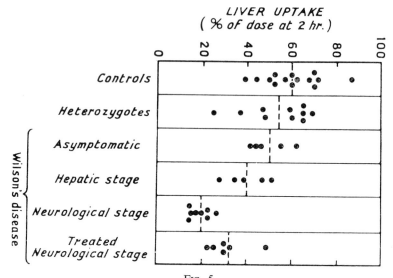

FIG. 5

The percentage of the injected dose of copper present in the liver at 2 hours. Again there is a steady falling off in the liver's ability to handle copper being most marked in the neurological stage of Wilson's disease and again showing improvement with treatment.

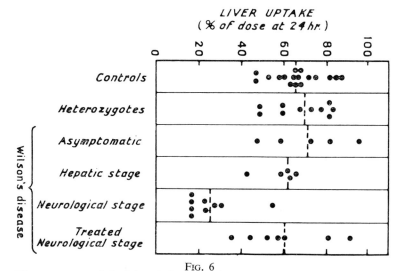

FIG. 6

The percentage of the injected dose of radiocopper in the liver at 24 hours. Controls, heterozygotes and asymptomatic subjects with Wilson's disease all take up over 60 per cent of the injected dose. There is a small fall off in the patients in the hepatic stage, but those with advanced neurological lesions show complete inability to concentrate cooper in the liver. After treatment there is a very great improvement in this function.

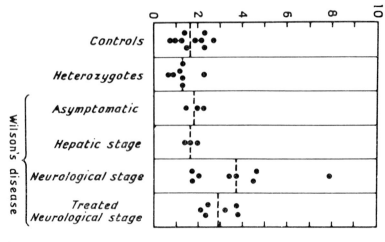

FIG. 7

The percentage of the injected radiocopper present in each litre of plasma at 2 hours after injection. This function is significantly disturbed only in those patients with advanced neurological disease. Again there is improvement with treatment.

noticeable here that the 2 hour time period gives a better separation than 24 hours (Figs. 5 and 6). This inability of the liver to clear injected copper is also shown in the measure of radioactivity present in the plasma at 2 hours after injection (Fig. 7). The response to treatment is also shown by these studies in that the patients with advanced disease who have received prolonged treatment return towards the normal levels of behaviour as measured by their ability to clear the plasma and concentrate the metal in the liver. Recently I have made a similar analysis of all the results of erythrocyte radioactivity. It is apparent from this that although the radio-activity in the red cells at 0·5 hour. 2 hours and 24 hours after injection is remarkably similar between Wilson's disease data (when all patients are included) and the control subjects, a breakdown of Wilson's disease patients so that the untreated cases are plotted separately shows that in these the uptake of copper by the red cells is depressed and the differences at 2 hours and 24 hours are statistically significant when compared with the group of Wilson's disease patients as a whole and also the controls. It would appear therefore that the erythrocytes in untreated Wilson's disease have an impaired ability to bind injected copper comparable to the liver (Fig. 8).

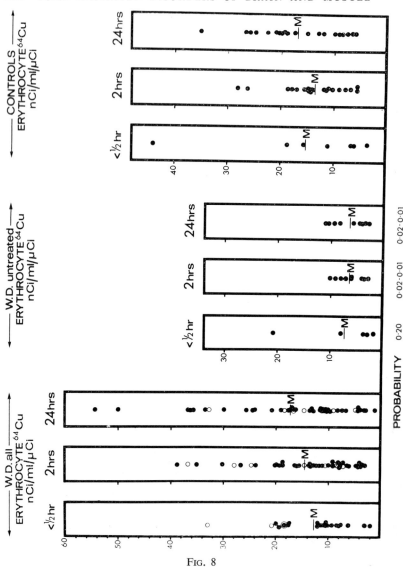

FIG. 8

Radioactivity expressed as nCi/ml. of washed red cells/μCi of radiocopper injected for all patients with Wilson's disease studied, for those studied before any treatment was given and for the controls. It will be seen that the mean red cell radioactivity in the untreated Wilson's disease patients are all low compared with the Wilson's disease group as a whole and the control subjects. The reduction of the untreated red cell activity below the other groups at 0·5 hr. is not statistically significant, but at 2 hr. and 24 hr. the probability is between 0·02 and 0·01 which is statistically significant.

The apparent clinical differences between hepatic and neurological forms of Wilson's disease does not make me believe that this is a disease caused by more than one abnormal gene, but that these are merely varying manifestations of the natural history of the condition and many patients go through a hepatic phase before developing typical neurological signs; some patients however die in the hepatic phase particularly when symptoms appeared before the age of puberty. Other patients develop what is apparently a purely neurological illness but if left untreated hepatic signs sooner or later make their presence felt. These studies with radioactive copper point to a progressive saturation of the liver with the metal leading eventually to involvement of other tissues, there being a particular predilection of the metal to deposit in the brain. Why some patients are able to undergo an apparent spontaneous arrest of the hepatic lesion later to develop the neurological lesion is not clear, but there must be additional factors in the environment and modifying genes which are involved. Although there are a number of unexplained facts such as a variable clinical picture and the variable caeruloplasmin concentrations there is in my view at present no evidence to suggest that Wilson's disease is not genetically homogeneous, although one must keep an open mind that such evidence may be found later.

Acknowledgments
I am indebted to the editor of *Brain* for permission to publish Fig. 3 which appeared in *Brain* **90** (1967) 161, and the editor of the *Lancet* for permission to publish Figs. 4, 5, 6 and 7 which appeared in the *Lancet* **1** (1967) 346.

REFERENCES
BEARN, A. G. (1960). A genetical analysis of thirty families with Wilson's disease (hepatolenticular degeneration). *Ann. hum. Gen.* **24**, 33.
OSBORN, S. B. & WALSHE, J. M. (1967). Studies with radioactive copper (^{64}Cu and ^{67}Cu) in relation to the natural history of Wilson's disease. *Lancet* **1**, 346.
STERNLIEB, I., MORELL, A. G., BAUER, C. D., COMBES, B., DE BOBES-STERNBERG, S., & SCHEINBERG, I. H. (1961). Detection of the heterozygous carrier of the Wilson's disease gene. *J. clin. Invest.* **40**, 707.

DISCUSSION OF PRESENTATION BY DR. WALSHE

Roth (Newcastle Upon Tyne). Is there any similarity in the age of onset of Wilson's Disease in affected members of the same family?

Walshe. The age of onset in the families tends to be close. Also in families the level of caeruloplasmin tends to run at the same level. This means that when vetting sibs you must know the level of caeruloplasmin in the affected patient before deciding whether the sib is affected.

Roth. Is it correct to say that the age of onset when all cases are considered extends over a large range but that in individual families the age of onset is very close?

Walshe. This is so.

Bower (Oxford). Is Penicillamine the only treatment?

Walshe. It is the only effective treatment.

Wilson (London). Is it true that Versene is inadequate?

Walshe. If you give it orally it is ineffective. If you give it intravenously then the patient develops side effects and it would mean an injection daily for life. I have used it on occasions.

Campbell (London). Is Penicillamine equally effective in cases with well established liver cirrhosis?

Walshe. Probably.

Campbell. In what dose?

Walshe. This is rather like asking how much Insulin you need to give a diabetic. Less than 1 gram is probably useless. I use at least 1·5 g. daily. A few years ago I had a patient on 1 gram and the Practitioner phoned to say the patient was worse. I suggested doubling the dose and following this the patient improved and indeed is going to Cambridge next term to read English. For effective treatment you look for improvement in general condition, improvement in results of tests and disappearance of the ring from around the iris.

Crome (Carshalton). Should vitamin B6 supplements be given?

Walshe. If the patient lived in the 'wilds' yes. Otherwise no.

Dickenson (Leeds). At what stage of the disease does renal involvement occur?

Walshe. I think at a very late stage. Certain patients have impaired ability to acidify the urine and produce ammonia. This is reversible with treatment if it is persevered with.

Burns. (Wolverley). Would you comment on the I.Q.

Walshe. In cases of untreated Wilson's disease, which are few, the I.Q. tends to deteriorate. The range of I.Q. in my experience was 70 to 148—average 105. One patient, the son of a doctor, has an I.Q. of 148. Another patient's I.Q. rose from 70 to 84 following treatment.

Walton (Newcastle). Have you any views on patients who have combined liver and cerebral lesions but whose copper is normal?

Walshe. No. Several papers describing this state of affairs have been written. Greenfield reported on this and confused the issue. Warlock & Nield also reported on it.

Walton. These cases do exist though?

Walshe. Yes. I am a great admirer of 'Winnie the Pooh' who had a very small brain and I believe in dabbling in one subject only!

CLINICAL ASPECTS OF INHERITED BRAIN DISORDERS

E. M. BRETT

IN the time available it is not possible to review the whole range of inherited brain disorders, and I shall limit myself to discussing certain aspects, particularly some of the recent advances in clinical and chemical understanding which are helping to make paediatric neurology one of the most interesting specialities today. Chemical and other advances are throwing light into previously dark corners and there is room for hope that these will in time illuminate a fuller understanding of many obscure disorders and allow successful treatment by diet and other means, as has already occurred in some of the inborn errors of metabolism.

Classification

The clinician might be justified in complaining that the classification of inherited brain disorders is becoming more difficult, rather than easier, with increasing knowledge. The ganglioside neurolipidoses are a case in point. With the exception of the rare congenital form and of Tay-Sachs' disease, which has usually a well-defined picture clinically and on investigation, the classification of the other forms of traditionally, but inappropriately, named 'amaurotic family idiocy' presents the paediatrician with a confusing welter of opposing views. The euphonious eponymous titles which are often used for these conditions read like a roll-call of the French Foreign Legion. The basic clinical criteria of age of onset, rate of evolution, presence and type of macular or retinal abnormality may vary from one affected member of a family to another.

This was the case in two sisters with neurolipidosis diagnosed by rectal biopsy and later proved at autopsy at the Hospital for Sick Children, Great Ormond Street, in whom the onset of symptoms was at 18 months in the first patient and 3·5 years in the second. There were no diagnostic ocular features, and it seems preferable to describe such cases by their age of onset rather than attempt at all costs to place them within a category, whether eponymous, 'late infantile' or 'early juvenile'.

The borderline between the ganglioside neurolipidoses and other related disorders may be blurred. Thus conditions have recently been recognized which appear intermediate between Tay Sachs' disease and Hurler's syndrome. Clinical and chemical features of Tay Sachs' disease were associated in one patient, who died at the age of two years, with the post-mortem finding of visceral changes resembling those of gargoylism (Norman *et al.*, 1964). Similar cases have since been reported by other authors. Salam & Idris (1964) reported a family in which a boy had Tay

141

Sachs' disease and his sister gargoylism, while four other siblings had died with histories suggesting similar conditions. Niemann-Pick disease and amaurotic family idiocy were reported in different members of a sibship by van Bogaert & Klein (1955). Features of both neurolipidosis and metachromatic leucodystrophy were found in a brain biopsy from a child examined at the Hospital for Sick Children, Great Ormond Street. Thieffry, Lyon & Maroteaux (1967) have recently reported the case of a boy with clinical, radiological and biochemical features of mucopolysaccharidosis who also showed evidence of a sulphatidosis, including reduced nerve conduction velocity, nerve biopsy changes and urinary findings.

Further difficulty in classification arises from the occurrence of formes frustes as is seen particularly in Hurler's syndrome. Young and his colleagues (1966) have recently reported the case of an adult with this condition who was of normal intelligence despite hydrocephalus and in whom no neuronal storage was found at autopsy. Ten patients were described by Scheie and his colleagues (1962) with a diffuse corneal haze in whom biopsy of skin, cornea and conjunctiva showed vacuolation as seen in Hurler's syndrome and the urine also contained mucopolysaccharides, although there were no other clinical features of gargoylism. The whole status of Hurler's syndrome and the related mucopolysaccharidoses is at present under review and a new classification has been suggested (Maroteaux & Lamy, 1965) with five separate subdivisions. Manley & Hawksworth (1966) believe it is possible to distinguish the autosomal from the sex-linked recessive form of Hurler's syndrome, the urine containing an excess of chondroitin sulphate in the former, and of both chondroitin and heparitin sulphate in the latter.

Norman, Forrester & Tingey (1967) have recently described a case of Niemann-Pick disease with slowly progressive neurological deterioration and marked cerebellar involvement, but with no clinical evidence of visceral involvement. The spleen at autopsy was only slightly enlarged, but showed the typical changes of Niemann-Pick disease. A rather similar case has recently been diagnosed by brain biopsy at the Hospital for Sick Children, Great Ormond Street, in which very slow intellectual deterioration had occurred over 4 years in a 9 year old boy and the diagnosis had not been suspected clinically.

Diagnosis

Dr. Holt, at the 1963 Sheffield symposium of this Society (Holt, 1964) stressed the importance of early detection of affected children in the presymptomatic phase of their illness. This, of course, is much easier in families where the disease has already been recognized in a sibling than when the patient is the first affected, and parental consanguinity will also alert the clinician to the possibility of recessively inherited disease.

Rarely the intrauterine onset of progressive cerebral disease can be inferred or suspected from the onset of epilepsy in the first few days of life in infants with microcephaly in a familial setting, as in the sibship of three described by Willi & Bischoff (1961) in which autopsy showed a disorder of myelination regarded as fitting into the category of a leucodystrophy. The intrauterine onset of convulsions was strongly suspected in three siblings born to consanguineous parents (Badr El Din, 1960) and familial intrauterine convulsions in three siblings have recently been described in pyridoxine dependency (Bejšovec, Kulenda, & Ponča, 1967).

The importance of a careful developmental and family history is nowhere greater than when dealing with suspected progressive brain disease. Because of the early onset of deterioration, dementia is all too often misinterpreted as amentia in the child with Tay Sachs' disease. In Krabbe's globoid body leucodystrophy, in which the onset of symptoms may be even earlier, with increasing stiffness and irritability, cerebral palsy is often diagnosed. Even when a sibling has been affected by a genetically-determined cerebral degenerative disorder, there may be delay in recognising that a later child is the victim of the same disease. Sometimes the parents may delude themselves, being unable to accept that tragedy could strike again, and on occasion the paediatrician, too, may seek to explain the child's developmental standstill or loss of skills as psychologically determined.

Careful examination will often, even in the early stages of such degenerative diseases, allow relative certainty as to the diagnosis. The characteristic cherry-red macular lesion is usually, but not invariably, present in Tay Sachs' disease. An exaggerated startle response to sound has been found to occur very early in the course of this disease, being present in all 17 patients studied by Schneck and his colleagues (1964) and the presenting symptom in 14, in whom it was noticed within the first two months of life.

The early diagnosis of tuberose sclerosis has recently become possible, before the appearance of adenoma sebaceum or other classical stigmata, with the recognition that depigmented skin lesions, leucoderma or 'vitiligo' may be very early manifestations of the disease (Gold & Freeman, 1965). These may possibly be present at birth and can often be seen at a few months of age, being more easily seen on the limbs in the summer months when they contrast more strongly with the child's darker surrounding skin. Similar lesions can often be found in smaller numbers on careful examination of apparently unaffected parents, siblings or other relatives, and their genetic implications are important since failure to recognise their significance may have led in the past to the sporadic occurrence of tuberose sclerosis and the mutation rate in the disease being overestimated. Infantile spasms, presumably occurring as a manifestation of tuberose sclerosis, are particularly frequent in children with depigmented naevi. Thus six out of seven of Gold & Freeman's patients with these skin lesions had infantile spasms, and Crichton (1966) found that 43 out of 174 children with spasms had skin anomalies, including nine with depigmented naevi, 11 with adenoma sebaceum, and 12 with cafe-au-lait spots. Careful scrutiny of the skin is therefore essential in cases of 'cryptogenic' infantile spasms and unexplained retardation.

Biochemical screening tests of urine and blood for various inborn errors of metabolism are well known, and their application and value have been discussed by Paine (1960) and Holt (1965), among others. Large-scale surveys of the populations of mental hospitals and other institutions have shown how many of these conditions have gone unrecognized. The classical survey by Carson & Neill (1962) in Northern Ireland yielded 58 cases of inborn errors from a population of 2081 studied, including 49 cases of phenylketonuria and two sisters with the previously unknown condition, homocystinuria. In this disease certain features suggestive of Marfan's syndrome, including lens dislocation and iridodonesis, are associated with developmental retardation, becoming apparent after the age of two or three years, and a tendency to spontaneous intravascular thrombosis. The latter has resulted in increasing neurological deficit or death in some patients and may be related to an abnormality of platelet stickiness (MacDonald et al., 1964). Schimke and his colleagues (1965) in the United States have screened urine from many patients with ectopia lentis and/or presumed Marfan's syndrome, and found 36 cases of homocystinuria in 20 families, some homocystinuric individuals being of normal intelligence.

The syndrome of hyperammonaemia with periodic vomiting and intellectual deterioration was first described in 1962 by Russell and his colleagues, and may well prove to be commoner than was first thought, since Rett (1966) in Austria found 21 girls with this clinical picture in a group of about 6,000 mentally retarded children. No abnormality of urine or liver function was found in these children, who had developed normally up to the age of about nine months, but a marked increase in the serum ammonia level was found in 17 patients studied. The condition is regarded as a sex-linked hereditary disease, and would seem to be much commoner in Austria than phenylketonuria, of which only eight cases were found in the same population.

Another example of a rare, recently recognized metabolic disorder with neurological manifestations is the syndrome of hyperuricaemia with mental defect, choreo-athetosis and self-mutilation. The early onset of motor deficit and retardation make this condition easily confused with nonprogressive cerebral palsy, as in the case of "Gout and cerebral palsy in a three-year-old boy" described by Riley (1960). The specific nature of the disorder and its biochemical features were first described in 1964 (Lesch & Nyhan; Nyhan, Oliver, & Lesch, 1965). Abnormally high levels of uric acid were found in all cases, and the daily excretion of uric acid approximates to that seen in adults with gout, while glycine has been shown to be converted to uric acid 200 times more rapidly than in normal controls.

Symptomless hyperuricaemia was found in males in three generations in one family.

It has been suggested (Clayton, Dobbs, & Patrick, 1967) that subacute necrotising encephalomyelopathy, first described by Leigh (1951) may be diagnosed by the finding of a raised blood pyruvate level. Clayton and her colleagues report three siblings with a similar history of deterioration with unusual features, in two of whom hyperpyruvaemia was found. One patient treated with lipoate showed an encouraging response with a fall in the blood pyruvate level.

In Tay Sachs' disease a valuable screening test has been found by American workers (Schneck, Maisel, & Volk, 1964; Volk, Aronson, & Saifer, 1964) to be a deficiency of the enzyme fructose-1-phosphate aldolase (F-1-PA) in the serum. Volk and his colleagues found that the enzyme could not be detected in the serum of 22 children with Tay Sachs' disease, nor in most of their parents, many of their grandparents and some of their healthy siblings. They suggest (Volk *et al.*, 1964) that the determination of serum F-1-PA may serve to identify the carrier state in this disease. Significantly increased serum levels of glutamic oxalacetic transaminase (GOT) and lactic dehydrogenase (LD) have also been found in the early stages of Tay Sachs' disease by Schneck and his colleagues.

It is unfortunate that similar enzyme abnormalities are not available for the diagnosis of neurolipidoses of later onset, since it is in these patients that the clinical picture is, in general, less clear than in Tay Sachs' disease. The E.E.G. may well prove of great value in this group since Pampiglione (1961) found marked photic sensitivity to low rates of flicker in cases of neurolipidosis other than Tay Sachs' disease. Recent experience at Great Ormond Street has shown a close correlation in several cases proved by biopsy.

It is in this group of patients that biopsy of neural tissue is often needed for a diagnosis. Cerebral biopsy has been in use for some years, but for various reasons this is not always acceptable to the parents of the child, and rectal biopsy provides a reliable alternative for certain diseases. The use of intestinal biopsy for the diagnosis of progressive degenerative brain disease was probably first suggested by Globus (1942), who described similar neuronal changes at autopsy, in a patient with amaurotic family idiocy, in the C.N.S. and myenteric plexuses. The first large series of rectal biopsies, in conditions other than Hirschsprung's disease, was that of Bodian & Lake (1963), who reported 49 biopsies with 11 positive diagnoses. Since that time many more biopsies have been performed at Great Ormond Street, and a series of 165 of these, carried out in the five-year period 1962-1966, has recently been reviewed (Brett & Berry, 1967). Thirty-three of these (20 per cent) showed positive diagnostic features. The two major diseases diagnosed were neurolipidosis (19 cases) and metachromatic leucodystrophy (11 cases). There were also two cases of Hurler's syndrome

G

and one of Niemann-Pick disease. Thirteen patients had both rectal and cerebral biopsies performed. In six of these both were negative, in six both positive, and in one case (of subacute sclerosing leuco-encephalitis) the cerebral biopsy was positive and the rectal negative. Autopsy confirmation of the diagnosis made on rectal biopsy was obtained in a further seven patients. In one patient rectal biopsy was performed at four days of age because of a family history of Tay Sachs' disease, and characteristic neuronal changes of this disease were seen; the child developed clinical evidence of the disease at the age of five months. From an analysis of this series, the indications for rectal biopsy appear more clearly than before; it is noteworthy that no positive biopsy was obtained in any patient without dementia, a family history of progressive degenerative brain disease, or other evidence pointing towards such disease. The patients with neuro-lipidoses other than Tay Sachs' disease were those in whom rectal biopsy was of greatest value, since diagnostic doubt was greatest among them, due to the lack of pathognomonic features clinically or on investigation.

In the 11 patients with metachromatic leucodystrophy, rectal biopsy was used mainly as a confirmatory test, since other investigations had given strong evidence of the diagnosis. This disease, regarded as a sulphatide lipidosis, is now known to be widespread in the body, involving the central and peripheral nervous systems, renal tract and gall bladder. As a result, many diagnostic methods are available. Examination of the urinary deposit will show metachromatically-staining intracellular material, and this has been found to be a very reliable test at Great Ormond Street, using the method of Lake (1965). Austin and his colleagues (Austin et al., 1964; Austin et al., 1966) have shown that urine from patients with metachromatic leucodystrophy is deficient in the enzyme arylsulphatase-A, for which sulphatide is the substrate. Metachromasia in salivary sediment and in biopsies of the parotid gland has been reported by Canelas and his colleagues (1964) in cases of Juvenile Metachromatic Leucodystrophy, but this finding does not seem to have been confirmed by other workers.

Peripheral nerve involvement was shown by Fullerton (1964) who found significant slowing of nerve conduction velocity in eight of nine case of metachromatic leucodystrophy examined. This is related to the duration of the illness and can be shown to increase with time, as in one recent case at Great Ormond Street. Peripheral nerve affection can sometimes be strongly suspected from the finding of absent or progressively decreased tendon reflexes, giving a clinical picture suggestive of polyneuritis, and Yudell and his colleagues (1967) at the Mayo Clinic compare the C.S.F. findings of increased protein without pleocytosis to the albumino-cytologic dissociation of the Guillain-Barré syndrome. Peripheral nerve biopsy was first used as a diagnostic test in metachromatic leucodystrophy by Thieffry & Lyon (1959), and it remains the most logical biopsy method in suspected cases, especially if nerve conduction velocity is slowed. In the 11 patients with metachromatic leucodystrophy, rectal biopsy was of value solely as a source of nerve fibres, and the same is true of dental pulp biopsy as suggested by Gardner & Zeman (1965) and also of Appendix Biopsy.

Peripheral nerve involvement has also recently been shown in Krabbe's globoid body leucodystrophy. Reduction or abolition of tendon reflexes has been seen in some patients with this disease at Great Ormond Street, while nerve conduction velocity was found to be reduced in several cases, nerve biopsy showing evidence of enzymatic abnormality.

Treatment

Until recently in most textbooks the section on the treatment of inherited brain disorders and neurometabolic diseases was limited to the statement that 'no treatment is of any avail'. With increasing understanding of the metabolic defects underlying these diseases, the hope of preventing deterioration is increasing. The dietary treatment of phenylketonuria and maple syrup urine disease are well known, but scarcely a week passes without the publication of a report or letter suggesting that a particular type of treatment may be of benefit in one or other neuro-metabolic disorder, and the paediatrician is often embarrassed to be asked by parents about a report in the latest number of a journal before he has read it himself.

The basic defect in homocystinuria was found, only two years after the disease was first recognized, to be a deficiency or absence of cystathionine synthetase (Mudd et al., 1964) and there is a possibility that a diet low in methionine and with added cystine might prevent the retardation, vascular lesions and perhaps lens dislocation, if started early. The experience of Komrower and his colleagues (1966) is encouraging in this respect. Homocystinuria was diagnosed in the newborn sister of two patients with this disease, the plasma methionine level rising to 26·8 mg./100 ml. on the ninth day, and a low methionine diet was started at once. At the age of two years and three months the child appeared normal, with none of the more serious stigmata of the disease. The diet was tried in an eight-year-old homocystinuric boy at Great Ormond Street but no improvement was seen in his low intellectual status or fit frequency, and it seems likely that the age at which dietary treatment begins is critical, as in phenylketonuria. Another recent approach to treatment has been by massive doses of pyridoxine and good biochemical results have been reported by some workers (Barber & Spaeth, 1967; Hooft, Carton, & Samyn, 1967).

Dietary treatment has been tried in hyperammonaemia, using various substances in the hope of regulating the blood ammonia level (Russell et al., 1962; Levin & Russell, 1967) but restriction of dietary protein seems to be the only practical treatment (Lorber, 1967). In the hyperuricaemic syndrome with retardation, choreo-athetosis and self-mutilation, treatment with probenecid, as for gout, has resulted in uric acid levels becoming normal, but in no clinical improvement. Leigh's encephalopathy may in time become treatable since, as mentioned above, a trial of lipoate in one case by Clayton and her colleagues gave encouraging results.

Refsum's disease, or Heredopathia atactica polyneuritiformis (H.A.P.) includes as its prominent features atypical retinitis pigmentosa, hypertrophic peripheral neuropathy, cerebellar ataxia and raised C.S.F. protein. The blood and tissues of patients have been shown to contain large amounts of phytanic acid, which is thought to accumulate as a result of a relative block in a pathway or pathways for its degradation or that of its esters. In a recent paper Eldjarn and his colleagues (1966) reported the results of a diet free from butter and vegetables and low in animal fats in two patients with H.A.P. By the end of a year the serum phytanic acid level had fallen markedly in both patients, and one of them was thought to show some clinical improvement while nerve conduction velocity in the ulnar nerve showed a slight increase. The results are inconclusive but encouraging, and vigorous dietary treatment started at any earlier stage of the disease, before the peripheral nerve involvement is well-developed, may perhaps prevent deterioration.

It would be wrong to close without mention of the supportive rôle of the paediatrician involved in the management of a child with one of the diseases in question. The progressive cerebral degenerative diseases produce some of the most tragic situations in medicine and the parents of their victims can indeed be said to have given hostages to fortune. The emotional and psychological problems of the parents and other family members, with their quota of anxiety, mourning, guilt, hostility and resentment, must be dealt with, and often the assistance of psychiatrist, medical social worker and other specialists is needed. The more incurable the disease, the more treatment aimed at palliation and adjustment of the environment is necessary. The diagnosis is not the end in these cases, but the beginning.

REFERENCES

AUSTIN, J., McAFEE, D., ARMSTRONG, D., O'ROURKE, M., SHEARER, L., & BACHHAWAT, B. (1964). Biochem. J., 93, 15C.

AUSTIN, J., ARMSTRONG, D., SHEARER, L., & McAFEE, D. (1966). Archs Neurol. Chicago, 14, 259.

BADR EL-DIN, M. K. (1960). J. Pediat. 56, 655.

BARBER, G. W. & SPAETH, G. L. (1967). Lancet, 1, 337.

BEJŠOVEC, M., KULENDA, Z., & PONČA, E. (1967). Archs Dis. Childh. 42, 201.

BODIAN, M. & LAKE, B. D. (1963). Br. J. Surg. 50, 702.

BOGAERT, L. VAN & KLEIN, D. (1955). J. Génét. hum. 4, 23.

BRETT, E. M. & BERRY, C. L. (1967). Br. Med. J. 3, 400.

CANELAS, H. M., ESCALANTE, O. D., IRIYA, K., & DE JORGE, F. B. (1964). Neuropsiquiat, S. Paulo 22, 122.

CARSON, N. A. J. & NEILL, D. W. (1962). Arch. Dis. Childh. 37, 505.

CLAYTON, B. E., DOBBS, R. H., & PATRICK, A. D. (1967). Archs Dis. Childh. 42, 467.

CRICHTON, J. U. (1966). Develop. Med. Child Neurol. 8, 273.

ELDJARN, L., TRY, K., STOKKE, O., MUNTHE-KAAS, D. W., STEINBERG, D., REFSUM, S., AVIGAN, J., & MIZE, C. (1966). Lancet, 1, 691.

FULLERTON, P. M. (1964). J. Neurol. Neurosurg. Psychiat. 27, 100.

GARDNER, D. G. & ZEMAN, W. (1965). *Develop. Med. Child Neurol.* **7**, 620.
GLOBUS, J. H. (1942). *J. Mt. Sinai Hosp.* **9**, 451.
GOLD, A. P. & FREEMAN, J. M. (1965). *Pediatrics, Springfield* **35**, 1003.
HOLT, K. S. (1964). *Neurometabolic Disorders in Childhood p.* 2. Edinburgh: Livingstone.
HOLT, K. S. (1965). *Develop. Med. Child Neurol.* **7**, 689.
HOOFT, C., CARTON, D., & SAMYN, W. (1967). *Lancet,* **1**, 1384.
KOMROWER, G., LAMBERT, A. M., CUSWORTH, D. C., & WESTALL, R. G. (1966). *Archs Dis. Childh.* **41**, 666.
LAKE, B. D. (1965). *Archs Dis. Childh.* **40**, 284.
LEIGH, D. (1951). *J. Neurol. Neurosurg. Psychiat.* **14**, 216.
LESCH, M. & NYHAN, W. L. (1964). *Am. J. Med.* **36**, 561.
LEVIN, B. & RUSSELL, A. (1967). *Am. J. Dis. Child.* **113**, 142.
LORBER, J. (1967). *Develop. Med. Child Neurol.* **9**, 232.
MANLEY, G. & HAWKSWORTH, J. (1966). *Archs Dis. Childh.* **41**, 91.
MAROTEAUX, P. & LAMY, M. (1965). *J. Pediat.* **67**, 312.
MCDONALD, L., BRAY, C., FIELD, C., LOVE, F., & DAVIES, B. (1964). *Lancet* **1**, 745.
MUDD, S. H., FINKELSTEIN, J. D., IRREVERRE, F., & LASTER, L. (1964). *Science, N.Y.* **143**, 1443.
NORMAN, R. M., TINGEY, A. H., NEWMAN, C. G. H., & WARD, S. P. (1964). *Archs Dis. Childh.* **39**, 634.
NORMAN, R. M., FORRESTER, R. M., & TINGEY, A. H. (1967). *Archs Dis. Childh.* **42**, 91.
NYHAN, W. L., OLIVER, W. J., & LESCH, M. (1965). *J. Pediat.* **67**, 257.
PAINE, R. S. (1960). *New Engl. J. Med.* **262**, 658.
PAMPIGLIONE, G. (1961). *VII. Internat. Congr. Neurol. Rome. Sept.* 1961. Soc. Graf. Romana, Vol. 1.
RETT, A. (1966). *Uber ein zerebral-atrophisches Syndrome bei Hyperammonämie.* Vienna: Verlag Brüder Hollinek.
RILEY, I. D. (1960). *Archs Dis. Childh.* **35**, 293.
RUSSELL, A., LEVIN, B., OBERHOLZER, V. G., & SINCLAIR, L. (1962). *Lancet,* **2**, 699.
SCHEIE, H. G., HAMBRICK, G. W., & BARNESS, L. A. (1962). *Am. J. Ophth.* **53**, 753.
SCHIMKE, R. N., MCKUSICK, V. A., HUANG, T., & POLLACK, A. D. (1965). *J. Am. med. Ass.* **193**, 711.
SCHNECK, L., MAISEL, J., & VOLK, B. W. (1964). *J. Pediat.* **65**, 749.
THIEFFRY, S. & LYON, G. (1959). *Revue neurol.* **100**, 452.
THIEFFRY, S., LYON, G., & MAROTEAUX, P. (1967). *Archs fr. Pédiat.* **24**, 425.
VOLK, B. W., ARONSON, S. M., & SAIFER, A. (1964). *Am. J. Med.* **36**, 481.
WILLI, H. & BISCHOFF, A. (1961). *Helv. paediat. Acta* **16**, 391.
YOUNG, G. F., WOLFE, H. J., BLENNERHASSETT, J. B., & DODGE, P. R. (1966). *Develop. Med. Child Neurol.* **8**, 37.
YUDELL, A., GOMEZ, M. R., LAMBERT, E. H., & DOCKERTY, M. B. (1967). *Neurology, Minneap.* **17**, 103.

DISCUSSION OF PRESENTATION BY DR. BRETT

Raine (Birmingham). We have recently been using pyridoxine in the management of homocystinuria but so far have not seen any improvement clinically in these cases. Have you any experience of this form of therapy?

Brett. We have used pyridoxine in a daily dose of 150 mg. in the treatment of homocystinuria but the period of observation of 2 months is too short for any conclusion to be made as to its effect.

Raine. Pyridoxine lowers the level of platelet stickiness. There seems to be little reason to give continuously the rather high doses (250-500 mg.) required to produce this effect. I would, however, consider it wise to utilise pyridoxine when the patient with homocystinuria is at increased risk for example as a cover in the event of operation or during periods of illness involving especially dehydration.

Brett. I would agree with your comment.

Burns (Wolverley). In patients with mental deficiency with areas of depigmentation, should tuberous sclerosis be considered?

Brett. To some extent it would depend on the number of such lesions present. Certainly in an infant with mental deficiency, spasms and depigmented skin lesions there should be a very high index of suspicion of tuberous sclerosis as the underlying disease.

THE GENETICS OF NEUROMUSCULAR DISORDERS

John Wilson

With the recent publication of two compendious treatises (McKusick, 1966; Pratt, 1967) for the first time in the English language there are systematic accounts embracing the genetics of neurological disorders, and I do not propose to attempt here to give what must necessarily be a truncated account of either book. Instead, I want to discuss in general terms certain facets, and some of the pitfalls in the study of the genetics of neuromuscular disorders.

There are few more arresting features in a clinical history than an account of a similar condition occurring in other relatives, and upon such evidence has grown much of our contemporary knowledge of the inheritance of disease. In the sphere of heredo-degenerative neurological disorders, this sort of information has accrued in haphazard fashion over the past century—some of it woefully inadequate, some of it misleading. Data has tended to be anecdotal rather than systematic and satisfactory population studies have been few.

Common omissions are to fail to record such important information as parental consanguinity, the total numbers in a sibship, the evidence for monozygosity or dizygosity in twins, whilst the too ready acceptance of second-hand information coloured by fantasy, surmise and wishful thinking of confused and embarrassed relatives is a common source of error. Whilst a lot of this implied criticism is levelled at the clinician, it is equally important that the clinical geneticist must be knowledgeable and critical about the nature of clinical problems. For example, the monumental study of hereditary optic atrophy in the *Treasury of Human Inheritance* (Bell, 1931) is spoiled by the uncritical inclusion of patients with unrelated conditions, for example syphilitic sea captains. An expertise with statistics does not exonerate the clinical geneticist from having an intimate clinical knowledge of the problem under study.

Some theoretical considerations in the study of hereditary neuro-muscular diseases

Autosomal dominant, autosomal recessive, and sex-linked recessive inheritance are well-known. In dominant conditions the heterozygote is not only usually affected himself (or herself) but also transmits the disease, whilst in autosomal recessive disorders heterozygous carriers are not generally affected, and the disease is only expressed in the homozygous state. That an underlying metabolic abnormality may be partly expressed in a heterozygote is evidenced by the slightly impaired tolerance to phenylalanine in phenylketonuria or the relative lowering of fructose 1,6-diphosphate aldolase in Tay Sachs' disease. It may be true that recessive and dominant conditions differ only in degree but this facile interpretation and its implications at the molecular level still await proof, at any rate in human diseases.

X-linked conditions provide a special case in that although heterozygous females do not suffer from the disease, there might be slight degrees of expression of the abnormal state through the possible random suppression of one or other X-chromosome. According to the hypothesis of Mary Lyon (1962), in females only one or other X-chromosome and its component genes operate in each cell, resulting in two cell populations differing only according to whether the maternally or paternally derived X-chromosome is sequestered. This may allow the expression of a genetically abnormal X-chromosome in an otherwise normal female. Whether or not this is the explanation of the reported histological and biochemical abnormalities in carriers of X-linked muscular dystrophy is not yet known, but this provides an interesting and plausible explanation.

Because of the anecdotal way in which genetic information has accumulated, dominant and X-linked conditions tend to be over-represented in the ordinary clinical literature, since the diseases described appear in each or alternate generations. It follows, too, that since many heredo-degenerative neurological disorders are fatal or totally incapacitating before the reproductive years, these cannot be potentiated in the community as dominant disorders. Notable exceptions to this are conditions such as dystrophia myotonica or tuberous sclerosis where the range of clinical variation, especially the age of presentation, is so wide that some patients do have an opportunity to reproduce. In the latter disease, it is also possible that there is in addition to a high mutation rate, a degree of clinical variation which allows the most mildly affected subjects to escape detection by a casual observer.

In general then, the incapacitating heredo-degenerative disorders which *characteristically* occur in early life are autosomal recessive conditions. The sphingolipidoses are uniformly inherited in this way, with the possible exception of Fabry's disease (angiokeratoma corporis diffusum). (Sweeley & Klionsky, 1963; Opitz *et al.,* 1965.)

In the later onset conditions, where other modes of inheritance are seen, there is much confusion. Dominant, sex-linked and autosomal recessive modes of inheritance are described for very many neurological diseases, not always on very substantial grounds. The major difficulty at present is to know whether or not the genetically different conditions are identical on an aetio-pathogenetic basis, especially at the molecular level.

If it is correct to assume that most, if not all, heredo-degenerative neuromuscular disorders are metabolically determined, it is of considerable theoretical importance to discover the relation between the differing genetic factors and the one disease. Unfortunately, it seems likely that the number of ways in which neuraxis and musculature can respond to metabolic insult is very limited, and a number of fundamentally distinct molecular abnormalities may result in a relatively homogeneous clinical and pathological picture. The usefulness of purely clinico-pathological criteria is therefore curtailed, and interpretation needs to be correspondingly cautious.

Lebers optic atrophy

Finally, I would like to describe a condition which does not readily fit into any of the schemes of inheritance discussed so far, and which is as fascinating for its neuropathological and biochemical aspects as it is for its genetic interest.

In Leber's hereditary optic atrophy, which is primarily a disease of the neuraxis, inheritance of the disease is solely through females (van Senus, 1963). Carrier females may themselves be affected, but in Europe this is predominantly a disease of males, comprising 85 per cent of the total. Interestingly in Japanese series, only 59 per cent of patients are male. Although this disease is sex-limited, it is certainly not sex-linked.

One possible explanation is that the condition is an autosomal dominant in which the genetic factor is lethal to affected spermatozoa, in this way ensuring that males only produce healthy offspring. The major difficulty in accepting this hypothesis is the number of pedigrees in which the proportion of affected males is considerably in excess of the 50 per cent expected on the Mendelian hypothesis. Furthermore, the comprehensive studies of van Senus (1963) in the Netherlands have also suggested that there is a considerable excess of carriers.

Two intriguing alternative explanations have been advanced. The first is that Leber's disease is a unique human example of cytoplasmic inheritance (Imai & Moriwaki, 1936). This would account for not only the excess of carriers, but also the excess of males.

The second, even more ingenious explanation is that the condition is not strictly genetically determined at all, but represents a stabilised transmissible disease, probably in the nature of a viral infection (Colenbrander, 1962). For this sort of condition, occurring as it does in the no-man's land between genetics and virology, the term 'episome' has been proposed. As yet, however, proof is lacking in this disease.

The study of this and other heredo-degenerative neurological disorders promises not only much of intrinsic genetic interest, but also to contribute to our understanding of fundamental problems of brain metabolism and disease processes.

REFERENCES

BELL, J. (1931). Anomalies and diseases of the eye. *Treasury of human inheritance. Eugen. Lab. Mem. XXVI. Vol. II*

COLENBRANDER, M. (1962). Observations on the heredity of Leber's disease. *Ophthalmologia, Basel,* **144**, 446.

IMAI, Y. & MORIWAKI, D. (1936). A probable case of cytoplasmic inheritance in man. A critique of Leber's disease. *J. Génét. hum.* **33**, 163.

LYON, M. F. (1962). Sex chromatin and gene action in the mammalian X-chromosome. *Am. J. hum. Genet.* **14**, 135.

McKUSICK, V. A. (1966). *Mendelian inheritance in Man.* London: Heinemann.

OPITZ, J. M., STILES, F. C., WISE, D., RACE, R. R., SANGER, R., VON GEMMINGEN, G. R., KIERLAND, R. R., CROSS, E. G., & DEGROOT, W. P. (1965). The genetics of angiokeratoma corporis diffusum (Fabry's disease) and its linkage relations with the Xg locus. *Am. J. hum. Genet.* **17**, 325.

PRATT, R. T. C. (1967). *The genetics of neurological disorders.* London: Oxford University Press.

SWEELEY, C. C. & KLIONSKY, B. (1963). Fabry's disease. Classification as a sphingolipidosis and partial characterization of a novel glycolipid. *J. biol. Chem.* **238**, 3148.

VAN SENUS, A. H. C. (1963). *Leber's disease in the Netherlands.* Doctorate Thesis, Leiden.